THE ULTIMATE
NEW ORLEANS SAINTS
TRIVIA BOOK

A Collection of Amazing Trivia Quizzes
and Fun Facts for Die-Hard Saints Fans!

Ray Walker

Exclusive Free Book

Crazy Sports Stories

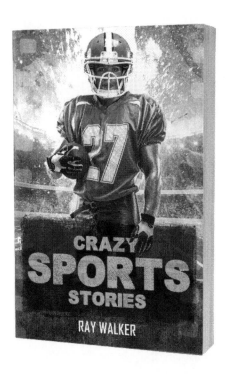

As a thank you for getting a copy of this book I would like to offer you a free copy of my book Crazy Sports Stories which comes packed with interesting stories from your favorite sports such as Football, Hockey, Baseball, Basketball and more.

Grab your free copy over at
RayWalkerMedia.com/Bonus

CONTENTS

INTRODUCTION

The New Orleans Saints were established in 1966 in New Orleans, Louisiana. The Boys from the Big Easy have consistently proven themselves to be a team who fights hard and is a force to be reckoned with in the NFL.

They currently hold 1 Super Bowl Championship, which they won in 2009. They have won 1 NFC Conference Championship, 6 NFC South Division Championships and 2 NFC West Division Championships. They are very often a threat in the NFC South, having last won it in 2019. They have made 13 NFL playoff appearances total, with their most recent Super Bowl appearance coming in Super Bowl XLIV.

The Saints have retired the uniform numbers of the Doug Atkins and Jim Taylor in addition to the many players they have inducted into their New Orleans Saints Hall of Fame and Ring of Honor.

The thing about football is that it is a lot like life. There are good times and bad times, good days and bad days, but you have to do your absolute best to never give up. The New Orleans Saints have proven that they refuse to give up and that they will do anything they need to do in order to bring a championship to the state of Louisiana. Winning is more than

1

possible when you have a storied past like the Saints do. They have so much captivating history and so many undeniable player legacies to be profoundly proud of.

The Saints currently call the Mercedes-Benz Superdome home, which opened in 1975. They play in one of the most difficult divisions in the NFL, the NFC South alongside the Atlanta Falcons, Carolina Panthers and Tampa Bay Buccaneers.

With such a rich past that goes back generations, you're probably already very knowledgeable as the die-hard Who Dat that you are. Let's test that knowledge to see if you truly are the World's Biggest Saints fan.

CHAPTER 1:

ORIGINS & HISTORY

QUIZ TIME!

1. Which of the following team names did the Saints franchise once go by?

    a. Pelicans

    b. Crawfish

    c. Jackrabbits

    d. None of the Above, they have always been the Saints

2. In what year was the New Orleans Saints franchise established?

    a. 1949

    b. 1956

    c. 1966

    d. 1969

3. The Saints' current home stadium is Mercedes-Benz Superdome.

    a. True

    b. False

4. Which division do the New Orleans Saints play in currently?

    a. NFC West
    b. AFC West
    c. NFC South
    d. AFC South

5. The New Orleans Saints were a member of the NFC West division from 1970-2001.

    a. True
    b. False

6. How many NFC Conference Championships have the Seahawks franchise won (as of the end of the 2019 season)?

    a. 0
    b. 1
    c. 2
    d. 3

7. What is the name of the Saints' mascot?

    a. Gumbo
    b. Sir Saint
    c. Saint Sam
    d. Both A & B

8. Who is the winningest head coach in New Orleans Saints history (as of 2020 season)?

    a. Jim E. Mora
    b. Sean Payton
    c. John North
    d. Bum Phillips

9. Which stadium was the first home stadium of the New Orleans Saints franchise?

    a. Louisiana Park
    b. Saints Stadium
    c. Tulane Stadium
    d. New Orleans Coliseum

10. Who was the first head coach of the New Orleans Saints' franchise?

    a. Hank Stram
    b. Ernie Hefferle
    c. J.D. Roberts
    d. Tom Fears

11. After Hurricane Katrina, the Saints played temporarily played at Tiger Stadium, the Alamodome and Giants Stadium.

    a. True
    b. False

12. What is the Saints' fight song?

    a. Hands of the Saints
    b. When the Saints Go Marching In
    c. Saint of Me
    d. Beast of All Saints

13. How many appearances has the New Orleans Saints' franchise made in the NFL playoffs (as of the end of the 2019 season)?

    a. 9
    b. 11

c. 13

d. 18

14. How many Super Bowl titles have the Saints won (as of the end of the 2019 season)?

    a. 0

    b. 1

    c. 2

    d. 3

15. The Saints never won an NFC West Division title during their time in the NFC West.

    a. True

    b. False

16. What is the Saints' cheerleaders squad called?

    a. The Saintsations

    b. The Saintettes

    c. The Gold Rush

    d. Saint Girls

17. How many NFC South Division titles have the New Orleans Saints won (as of the end of the 2019 season)?

    a. 3

    b. 6

    c. 8

    d. 9

18. Who is the current head coach of the New Orleans Saints?

    a. Jim Haslett

    b. Jim E. Mora

    c. Mike Ditka

    d. Sean Payton

19. Drew Brees is the current quarterback of the New Orleans Saints (as of the 2020 season).

    a. True

    b. False

20. The name "Saints" is a reference to the jazz music heritage of New Orleans.

    a. True

    b. False

QUIZ ANSWERS

1. D – None of the Above, they have always been the Saints

2. C – 1966

3. True

4. C – NFC South

5. A – True

6. B – 1 (2009)

7. D – Both A & B

8. B – Sean Payton

9. C – Tulane Stadium

10. D – Tom Fears

11. True

12. B – When the Saints Go Marching In

13. C – 13

14. B – 1

15. B – False, (1991 and 2000)

16. A - The Saintsations

17. B – 6

18. D – Sean Payton

19. A – True

20. A – True

DID YOU KNOW?

1. The Saints franchise has had 13 head coaches so far in their history. They include: Tom Fears, J.D. Roberts, John North, Ernie Hefferle, Hank Stram, Dick Nolan, Bum Phillips, Wade Phillips, Jim E. Mora, Rick Venturi, Mike Ditka, Jim Haslett and Sean Payton.

2. The Saints' current head coach is Sean Payton. He began his coaching career as an offensive assistant at San Diego State University. He was named the Saints' head coach in 2006. Payton has the second longest tenure among active head coaches behind Bill Belichick who has been the head coach of the New England Patriots since 2000. Payton is the Saints' all-time winningest head coach with a current record of 134-79-0. In 2006, he was named the AP Coach of the Year.

3. The Saints' current playoff record is 9-12. They made the playoffs most recently in 2017, 2018 and 2019.

4. In 2013, 3 players were the first to be inducted into the Saints Ring of Honor and have their numbers retired by the team: Archie Manning (#8), Rickey Jackson (#57) and Willie Roaf (#77). The Saints Ring of Honor now also includes Morten Andersen, Tom Benson and Will Smith.

5. New Orleans/the Saints have hosted the Super Bowl 10 times: IV in 1970, VI in 1972, IX in 1975, XII in 1978, XV in 1981, XX in 1986, XXIV in 1990, XXXI in 1997, XXXVI in

2002 and XLVII in 2013. The Mercedes-Benz Superdome is set to host Super Bowl LVIII in 2024. The one Super Bowl they won was held at Sun Life Stadium in Miami Gardens, Florida.

6. The name "Saints" is an allusion to the team's foundation date, November 1, being All Saints' Day in the Catholic faith as New Orleans has a large Catholic population.

7. The New Orleans Saints have made 1 Super Bowl appearance in franchise history... so far. They won the only Super Bowl they have appeared in. In Super Bowl XLIV, they faced the Indianapolis Colts at Sunlife Stadium in Miami Gardens, Florida. The New Orleans Saints are one of only three NFL teams to win their sole Super Bowl Appearance. The other two teams are the Tampa Bay Buccaneers and the New York Jets.

8. The current owner of the New Orleans Saints is Gayle Benson. She is also the owner of the NBA's New Orleans Pelicans. She is one of ten female NFL team owners.

9. The New Orleans Saints currently are a part of the NFC South alongside the Atlanta Falcons, Carolina Panthers and Tampa Bay Buccaneers. They were previously a member of the NFC West.

10. Will Smith is the latest Saint to have his number retired by the team. His number 91 was retired in 2019. Smith played for the Saints from 2004-2012.

CHAPTER 2:

JERSEYS & NUMBERS

QUIZ TIME!

1. Original majority owner of the Saints, John W. Mecom Jr.'s preference was to have the team's color scheme consist of "Mecom Blue", a shade which was used by all of his other investments. Yet, the NFL informed him that it too closely resembled the blue used by the _____.

   a. New York Giants
   b. San Diego Chargers
   c. New England Patriots
   d. Buffalo Bills

2. The Saints' current team colors are _____, _____, and _____.

   a. Old Gold, Oil Black, and Wedding Dress White
   b. Gold, Oil Black, and White
   c. Old Gold, Black, and Mecom Blue
   d. Old Gold, Black, and White

3. The Saints wore black helmets during the 1969 preseason, but NFL commissioner Pete Rozelle banned the team from using them during the regular season, since Mecom did not notify the league of the uniform change.

    a. True

    b. False

4. Which of the following numbers in NOT retired by the New Orleans Saints (as of the 2019 season)?

    a. 12

    b. 31

    c. 81

    d. All of the Above

5. What uniform number does QB Drew Brees currently wear as a member of the Saints?

    a. 5

    b. 8

    c. 9

    d. 10

6. What uniform number did Rickey Jackson wear during his time with the Saints?

    a. 44

    b. 57

    c. 67

    d. 75

7. Doug Atkins' No. 81 was retired by the Saints in 1969.

    a. True

    b. False

8. What uniform number did Jahri Evans wear during his time with the Saints?

    a. 43
    b. 53
    c. 63
    d. 73

9. What uniform number did Archie Manning wear during his time with the Saints?

    a. 2
    b. 4
    c. 8
    d. 10

10. Archie Manning's uniform number is retired by the New Orleans Saints.

    a. True
    b. False

11. What uniform number did Willie Roaf wear during his time with the Saints?

    a. 88
    b. 77
    c. 66
    d. 55

12. What uniform number did Pat Swilling wear during his time with the Saints?

    a. 53
    b. 54

c. 55

d. 56

13. Alvin Kamara currently wears the No. 41 for the New Orleans Saints.

    a. True

    b. False

14. What uniform number does Cameron Jordan currently wear for the Saints?

    a. 84

    b. 88

    c. 94

    d. 98

15. What uniform number did Dave Waymer wear during his time with the Saints?

    a. 66

    b. 69

    c. 76

    d. 79

16. What uniform number did Eugene Robinson wear during his time with the Seahawks?

    a. 40

    b. 43

    c. 44

    d. 48

17. What uniform number did Marques Colston wear during his time with the Saints?

a. 12

b. 22

c. 32

d. 42

18. What uniform number did Sam Mills wear during his time with the Saints?

    a. 31

    b. 41

    c. 51

    d. 61

19. What uniform number did Wayne Martin wear during his time with the Saints?

    a. 91

    b. 93

    c. 95

    d. 98

20. The Saints debuted white pants in 1975, coinciding with their move to the Superdome.

    a. True

    b. False

QUIZ ANSWERS

1. B – San Diego Chargers

2. D – Old Gold, Black, and White

3. A – True

4. A – 12

5. C – 9

6. B – 57

7. A – True

8. D – 73

9. C – 8

10. B – False

11. B – 77

12. D – 56

13. True

14. C – 94

15. D – 79

16. C – 44

17. A – 12

18. C – 51

19. B – 93

20. A – True

DID YOU KNOW?

1. The Saints have retired 2 players and their numbers overall so far: Jim Taylor (No. 31) and Doug Atkins (No. 81). Members of the New Orleans Saints' Ring of Honor include: Archie Manning, Rickey Jackson, Willie Roaf, Morten Anderson, Will Smith and Tom Benson.

2. During his time with the Saints, Stan Brock wore the uniform No. 67.

3. During his time with the Saints, Reggie Bush wore the uniform No. 25.

4. During his time with the Saints, Morten Anderson wore the uniform No. 7.

5. From 1986 through 1995, the sleeves of the Saints' jerseys and sides of their pants featured a logo with a fleur-de-lis inside an outline of the state of Louisiana. That logo was removed in 1996 and replaced with a fleur-de-lis on both the sleeves and sides of their pants.

6. From 1996 through 1998, the Saints used gold numbers on both their white and black uniforms. They were changed to black in 1999 after complaints of the gold numbers being too difficult to read.

7. During his time with the Saints, Will Smith wore the uniform No. 91.

8. Malcom Jenkins has worn the uniform No. 27 both during

his previous stint with the Saints and currently with the Saints.

9. During his time with the Saints, Devery Henderson wore the uniform No. 19.

10. During his time with the Saints, Deuce McAllister wore the uniform No. 26.

CHAPTER 3:

FAMOUS QUOTES

QUIZ TIME!

1. Which Saints player once said: "I needed New Orleans so badly back in 2006, just somebody to believe in me, somebody to care about me."?

    a. Reggie Bush
    b. Deuce McAllister
    c. Marques Colston
    d. Drew Brees

2. Which former Saints player once said: "Taking care of my parents is one of the things that I want to do, just give them some of the things that we never had a chance to have. It's all about remembering where I came from."?

    a. Mark Ingram
    b. Reggie Bush
    c. Jimmy Graham
    d. Jahri Evans

3. Drew Brees once said: "Winners, I am convinced, imagine their dreams first. They want it with all their heart and expect it to come true. There is, I believe, no other way to win."

    a. True
    b. False

4. Which Saints head coach once said: "To do things you've never done before, you have to do things you've never done before."?

    a. Jim Mora
    b. Bum Phillips
    c. Sean Payton
    d. Hank Stram

5. Which former Saints player once said: "Outside of being passionate and knowledgeable fans, Saints fans are really good people. It's a great environment to be a part of."?

    a. Willie Roaf
    b. Jahri Evans
    c. Marques Colston
    d. Jimmy Graham

6. Which former Saints player is quoted as saying: "The atmosphere in New Orleans is always great, especially on Sundays. If the end zone wall wasn't so high, I would jump up there with them."?

    a. Darren Sproles
    b. Devery Henderson

c. Pierre Thomas

d. Courtney Roby

7. Which former Saints player is quoted as saying: "I always tell kids; you can do whatever you put your mind to. You can do whatever you want to do in your life, but it starts with you believing in yourself."?

a. Pierre Thomas

b. Devery Henderson

c. Chris Ivory

d. Malcolm Jenkins

8. Former Saints player, Archie Manning once said, "Pressure is something you feel when you don't know what the hell you're doing."

a. True

b. False

9. Which Saints head coach once said: "You fail all the time, but you aren't a failure until you start blaming someone else."?

a. Jim Haslett

b. Mike Ditka

c. Wade Phillips

d. Bum Phillips

10. Which former Saints player once said: "You can't be 100% perfect but try to evaluate things and do what's right. If you make every effort to do the right thing, you'll come out ok. It comes down to priorities and making good decisions."?

a. Archie Manning

b. Tony Galbreath

c. Chuck Muncie

d. Tom Myers

11. Which Saints player is quoted as saying: "I just want to go out there and work as hard as I can to be the best player I can be and help this team win a championship. That's my ultimate goal"?

a. Willie Snead

b. Mark Ingram

c. Vonn Bell

d. Cameron Jordan

12. Which Saints coach is quoted as saying, "We owe it to our fans. Our fans have always been there for us. We want the people of New Orleans, Louisiana and the Gulf Coast region to be proud of us. We are going to give them our best."?

a. Wade Phillips

b. Joe Vitt

c. Jack Del Rio

d. Sam Mills

13. Which former Saints player is quoted as saying: "Everyone knows the goal – to get to the Super Bowl. No matter what else is going on, guys know that is the thing we play for."?

a. Thomas Morstead

b. Mike Bell

c. Will Smith

d. Reggie Bush

14. Which Saints player is quoted as saying: "The goal is always the Super Bowl. That's what we play for. To have it in New Orleans only motivates us to work harder for the ultimate prize."?

    a. Malcolm Jenkins
    b. Alvin Kamara
    c. Deonte Harris
    d. Janoris Jenkins

15. Which former Saints player is quoted as saying: "The Saints expect a lot of me and I expect a lot of myself too. The reason why I came here is to win a championship and that is what everyone's expectations are."?

    a. Jimmy Graham
    b. Curtis Lofton
    c. Drew Brees
    d. Jahri Evans

16. Former Saint, Willie Roaf once said, "If you aren't going all the way, why go at all?".

    a. True
    b. False

17. Which former Saints player is quoted as saying: "With our offense, it's hard to really stop one person because if you're focusing on one person, Colston is going to go out there and light it up. Or Sproles. Or Henderson."?

    a. Mark Ingram
    b. Drew Brees

c. Pierre Thomas

d. Jimmy Graham

18. "Do I still got a fleur de lis on my helmet? Alright then." - _____ when asked about his Super Bowl expectations.

    a. Alvin Kamara

    b. Emmanuel Sanders

    c. Latavius Murray

    d. Taysom Hill

19. "Who _____?"

    a. That

    b. Here

    c. Dat

    d. Cares

20. Drew Brees once said: "No matter where in the world you go, New Orleans is always a part of you."

    a. True

    b. False

QUIZ ANSWERS

1. D – Drew Brees

2. B – Reggie Bush

3. B – False, Joe Montana

4. C – Sean Payton

5. C – Marques Colston

6. A – Darren Sproles

7. A – Pierre Thomas

8. False, Peyton Manning

9. D – Bum Phillips

10. A – Archie Manning

11. B – Mark Ingram

12. B – Joe Vitt

13. C – Will Smith

14. A – Malcolm Jenkins

15. B – Curtis Lofton

16. B – False, Joe Namath

17. D – Jimmy Graham

18. A – Alvin Kamara

19. C - Dat

20. A – True

DID YOU KNOW?

1. "New Orleans is just a doggone fun place to be." – Archie Manning

2. "The Saints and the city of New Orleans are going to fight together. No matter what is thrown at us, we are going to fight and stand tall." – Pierre Thomas

3. "This city has become my home and this organization has been woven into the fabric of this city." – Steve Gleason

4. "Each and every year when people see the Saints on their calendar, they've got to get their mind right because we're a team that believes we can win every time we step on the field and should win every time we step on the field, no matter who we're playing against." – Drew Brees

5. "When you wake up, think about winning the day. Don't worry about a week or a month from now – just think about one day at a time." – Drew Brees

6. "One time the coach called me on the phone and said, 'Doug I hear you are not happy with our team and that you want to be traded.' I said "Coach that is fine." He said he would call and see it anybody wanted me and would call me back. Later he called me back and said 'Doug, I traded you to New Orleans.' I said 'Coach, thank you.' And I enjoyed three years with the Saints organization, and they are fine people with fine fans. – Doug Atkins in his Pro Football Hall of Fame Induction Address

7. " Until the very end Jim Finks was known as a former Steeler, Viking, Bear, but it is no coincidence he left this world a Saint. – Jim Finks Jr. on behalf of his father Jim Finks in his Pro Football Hall of Fame Induction Address

8. "As a result of the hard work at Louisiana Tech, the New Orleans Saints, Tom Benson, and general manager Jim Finks and head coach Jim Mora drafted me in the first round. I was blessed to have nine wonderful years with the Saints organization, especially winning our first playoff game in the 2000 season. I will forever be thankful to the Saints for drafting me." – Willie Roaf in his Pro Football Hall of Fame Induction Address

9. "My owner, he went one time and then won. We go back again this year, we win. I think he should be up for the Hall of Fame. Not only that, I mean, keeping the Saints in New Orleans. The Saints went through Katrina. They come back, go through the oil spill now. None of that would have been a disaster. If they lost the Saints, it would have been ten times worse than all that, so I take my hat off to them. A lot of people say why you pick Mr. Benson do this or that? Ain't nobody for New Orleans than the Saints and Mr. Benson because he is the one who kept the Saints in New Orleans. I tell you what, a lot of teams left in the middle of the night taking their teams other places. He could have did the same thing that some of the other guys did. You got to take your hat off to somebody when they doing right, and I take my hat off to him. He could have took the Saints and moved them to California or San

Antonio. If Katrina did us like that, oil spill did us like that, imagine losing the Saints." – Rickey Jackson in his Pro Football Hall of Fame Induction Address

10. "I owe Coach Bum Phillips a huge tip of the 10-gallon hat. He had patience with me when I started my NFL career in New Orleans, and he stuck with me until we got it right. Bum was always good for a good story and a lot of laughs. When John Mecom owned the team, he wanted to be more involved and asked Bum how he could help. Bum looked at him, paused, and said, "Well, you're the owner, so own." And that was that. Bum cared about his players. In meetings, he'd talk about life, how to be a good guy, how to help others. He taught me the value of giving back to the community. I'm proud to have started Kicks for Kids in New Orleans. We helped Children's Hospital and raised a lot of money." – Morten Anderson in his Pro Football Hall of Fame Induction Address

CHAPTER 4:

CATCHY NICKNAMES

QUIZ TIME!

1. What nickname does Drew Brees NOT go by?

   a. Breesus

   b. Saint Drew

   c. Cool Brees

   d. Hurricane Drew

2. Rickey Jackson goes by the nickname, "City Champ".

   a. True

   b. False

3. What nickname does Willie Roaf go by?

   a. Dopey

   b. Looney

   c. Crazy

   d. Nasty

4. Archie is a nickname. What is Archie Manning's full name?

a. Elisha Archibald Manning

b. Archibald Elisha Manning

c. Elijah Archibald Manning

d. Archibald Elijah Manning

5. Which is a popular nickname the Saints as a team have been referred to as?

   a. The Marching Ins

   b. The Gold Wave

   c. The Who Dats

   d. The Saint Men

6. What was the nickname for the Saints linebacker corps in the 1980's and 1990's?

   a. The Gold Patrol

   b. The Dome Patrol

   c. The New Orlinebackers

   d. The Who Dat Patrol

7. Marques Colston goes by the nickname, "The Quiet Storm".

   a. True

   b. False

8. What nickname does Taysom Hill go by?

   a. Hills are Alive

   b. Over the Hill

   c. The Taysom Missile

   d. The Mormon Missile

9. What nickname does Reggie Bush go by?

    a. Runnin' Reggie
    b. Reginator
    c. Swoosh
    d. Bushy

10. What nickname does Thomas Morstead go by?

    a. More Leg
    b. The Leg
    c. More Punts
    d. Tommy Legs

11. What nickname does Morten Andersen go by?

    a. Golden Retriever
    b. Husky
    c. Great Dane
    d. German Shepherd

12. The Saints cheerleaders go by the nickname "The Saintsations".

    a. True
    b. False

13. What nickname did Doug Atkins go by?

    a. Skinny
    b. Tiny
    c. Little
    d. Big

14. What nickname did Earl Campbell go by?

    a. The Earl Flower

    b. The Tyler Flower

    c. The Earl Rose

    d. The Tyler Rose

15. Mark Ingram and Alvin Kamara are sometimes referred to as "Boom and Zoom".

    a. True

    b. False

16. Ken Stabler went by the nickname _____.

    a. Lizard

    b. Snake

    c. Iguana

    d. Praying Mantis

17. Former Saint, Will Smith went by the nickname "The Fresh Prince" due to having the same name as actor, Will Smith.

    a. True

    b. False

18. The offense Stan Brock developed was nicknamed "_____".

    a. The Brock Bone

    b. The Brock Back

    c. The Brock Boys

    d. Brock & Roll

19. What nickname does Teddy Bridgewater go by?

    a. Bridgey
    b. Teddy Bear
    c. Gump
    d. The Water Boy

20. "Deuce" McAllister's given full name is Dulymus Jenod McAllister.

    a. True
    b. False

QUIZ ANSWERS

1. B – Saint Drew

2. True

3. D – Nasty

4. A - Elisha Archibald Manning

5. C – The Who Dats

6. B – The Dome Patrol

7. A – True

8. D – The Mormon Missile

9. C – Swoosh

10. B – The Leg

11. C – Great Dane

12. A – True

13. B – Tiny

14. D – The Tyler Rose

15. A – True

16. B – Snake

17. B – False

18. A – The Brock Bone

19. C – Gump

20. A – True

DID YOU KNOW?

1. "Hokie" is a nickname. Hokie Gajan's full name was Howard Lee Gajan Jr.

2. Former Saints player Jimmy Graham goes by the nickname "Avatar".

3. Former Saints, Chuck Munice and Tony Galbreath were together nicknamed "Thunder and Lightning".

4. "Bum" is a nickname. Bum Phillips' full name was Oail Andrews Phillips.

5. Former Saints player, Sam Mills went by the nickname "Field Mouse".

6. Former Saints player, Bobby Hebert goes by the nickname "Cajun Cannon".

7. Former Saints player, Joe Horn goes by the nickname "Hollywood".

8. "Aints" was a nickname given to the 1980 Saints who went 1-15.

9. Saints player, Latavius Murray goes by the nickname "Tay Train".

10. "Turk" is a nickname. Turk McBride's full name is Claude Maurice McBride.

CHAPTER 5:

BREESUS

QUIZ TIME!

1. What is Drew Brees' full name?

    a. Andrew Michael Brees

    b. Michael Andrew Brees

    c. Andrew Christopher Brees

    d. Christopher Andrew Brees

2. As of the 2020 season, Drew Brees has played his entire NFL career with the New Orleans Saints.

    a. True

    b. False

3. Where was Drew Brees born?

    a. Nashville, Tennessee

    b. San Jose, California

    c. Denver, Colorado

    d. Dallas, Texas

4. When was Drew Brees born?

    a. January 15, 1985
    b. January 15, 1979
    c. March 15, 1979
    d. March 15, 1985

5. In a 2012 Super Bowl Pepsi commercial, Drew Brees appeared alongside which popular band?

    a. Maroon 5
    b. The Rolling Stones
    c. One Direction
    d. Jonas Brothers

6. How many total Pro Bowls has Drew Brees been named to in his career so far (as of the end of the 2019 season)?

    a. 7
    b. 9
    c. 11
    d. 13

7. Where did Drew Brees go to college?

    a. Purdue University
    b. University of Kentucky
    c. Texas A&M University
    d. Ohio State Univeristy

8. Drew Brees was drafted by the New Orleans Saints in the 2nd round of the 2001 NFL Draft.

    a. True
    b. False

9. How many times has Drew Brees won the ESPN ESPY Award for Best Record-Breaking Performance?

   a. 0
   b. 1
   c. 2
   d. 3

10. Which sports magazine named Drew Brees their 2010 Sportsman of the Year?

    a. Sports Illustrated
    b. ESPN the Magazine
    c. Sporting News
    d. Football Digest

11. What is the name of Drew Brees' book released in July of 2010?

    a. Drew Brees: Coming Back Stronger
    b. Coming Back Stronger: Unleashing the Hidden Power of Adversity
    c. Drew Brees: Unleashing the Hidden Power of Adversity
    d. Unleashing the Hidden Power of Adversity: The Drew Brees Story

12. Drew Brees was on the cover of the NFL Madden 2011 video game.

    a. True
    b. False

13. What year was Drew Brees named the NFL Comeback Player of the Year?

    a. 2004
    b. b. 2006
    c. c. 2007
    d. d. 2010

14. Drew and his wife, Brittany have a charity called the "Brees Dream Foundation".

    a. True
    b. False

15. How many times was Drew Brees named the Big Ten Offensive Player of the Year?

    a. 0 times
    b. 1 time
    c. 2 times
    d. 3 times

16. What year was Drew Brees named the Walter Payton NFL Man of the Year?

    a. 2002
    b. 2004
    c. 2006
    d. 2010

17. Drew Brees won the Super Bowl XLIV MVP Award.

    a. True
    b. False

18. How many Super Bowl Championships has Drew Brees won during his career so far (as of the end of the 2019 season)?

    a. 0
    b. 1
    c. 2
    d. 3

19. Drew Brees currently wears the uniform No ___.

    a. 90
    b. 39
    c. 19
    d. 9

20. Drew Brees currently holds the NFL record for most career passing yards.

    a. True
    b. False

QUIZ ANSWERS

1. C - Andrew Christopher Brees

2. B – False, San Diego Chargers 2001-2005

3. D – Dallas, Texas

4. B - January 15, 1979

5. C – One Direction

6. D – 13

7. A – Purdue University

8. B – False, San Diego Chargers

9. C – 2 (2012 and 2019)

10. A – Sports Illustrated

11. B – Coming Back Stronger: Unleashing the Hidden Power of Adversity

12. A – True

13. A – 2004

14. A – True

15. C – 2 times

16. C – 2006

17. A - True

18. B – 1

19. D – 9

20. A – True

DID YOU KNOW?

1. Drew Brees was selected as the Grand Marshal of the Krewe of Bacchus in the 2007 Mardi Gras Parade in New Orleans.

2. In June 2010, President Barack Obama appointed Drew Brees to be a co-chair on the President's Council on Fitness, Sports and Nutrition.

3. Drew Brees is one of the eight quarterbacks to hold the NFL record for most touchdown passes in a single game with the 13 total each. The other quarterbacks tied with Brees currently are Sid Luckman (Chicago Bears), Adrian Burk (Philadelphia Eagles), George Blanda (Houston Oilers), Y.A. Tittle (New York Giants), Joe Kapp (Minnesota Vikings), Peyton Manning (Denver Broncos) and Nick Foles (Philadelphia Eagles).

4. In 2009, Drew Brees was inducted into Purdue University's Intercollegiate Athletics Hall of Fame. He was named the Big Ten's best quarterback of the 90's.

5. Drew Brees won a Bert Bell Award in 2009, which is given to the NFL player of the year.

6. Drew Brees wears the uniform No. 9 to honor baseball legend, Ted Williams who donned the same uniform number.

7. When Sports Illustrated Drew Brees as their 2010 Sportsman of the Year, they said the award was "for not

only leading the New Orleans Saints to the first Super Bowl title in the franchise's history, but also for helping lead the city of New Orleans' rebirth after the tragedy of Hurricane Katrina".

8. Drew Brees has many food allergies, so he does not eat dairy, gluten or nuts.

9. Major NFL records held by Drew Brees currently include: Most career passing touchdowns, Most career passing yards, Most career pass completions, Most career pass attempts, Highest career completion percentage, Most pass completions in a season, Highest single-season completion percentage, Highest single-game completion percentage, Most touchdown passes in a game (tied) and Most consecutive games with a touchdown pass.

10. Drew Brees was named the Associated Press Male Athlete of the Year in 2010.

CHAPTER 6:

STATISTICALLY SPEAKING

QUIZ TIME!

1. Marques Colston holds the New Orleans Saints franchise record for the most career receiving touchdowns with _____ total.

    a. 70
    b. 72
    c. 78
    d. 80

2. Alvin Kamara holds the New Orleans Saints franchise record for the most receiving touchdowns in a season with 14 total in 2018.

    a. True
    b. False

3. Mark Ingram holds the New Orleans Saints franchise record for the most career rushing touchdowns with _____ total.

    a. 30
    b. 40

c. 50

d. 60

4. The New Orleans Saints record for most points scored in a single season is _____ in 2011.

    a. 527

    b. 537

    c. 547

    d. 557

5. New Orleans Saints quarterback Drew Brees holds the Saints' record for most career pass attempts with _____ total.

    a. 3,794

    b. 5, 742

    c. 7,653

    d. 8, 352

6. 6. On November 10, 2013 vs. the Dallas Cowboys, the New Orleans Saints set a single game record for most first downs with ____ total.

    a. 35

    b. 40

    c. 45

    d. 50

7. Drew Brees holds the New Orleans Saints career record for games played with 216 (so far).

    a. True

    b. False

8. Michael Thomas holds the single season New Orleans Saints and NFL record for most receptions with _____ total in 2019.

    a. 119

    b. 129

    c. 139

    d. 149

9. Morten Anderson holds the New Orleans Saints career record for most field goal attempts with _____ total.

    a. 369

    b. 379

    c. 389

    d. 399

10. Dave Waymer holds the New Orleans Saints career record for most passes intercepted with _____ total.

    a. 27

    b. 37

    c. 47

    d. 57

11. Rickey Jackson holds the New Orleans Saints career record for most quarterback sacks with _____ total.

    a. 123

    b. 234

    c. 345

    d. 456

12. Drew Brees holds the New Orleans Saints single season record for most consecutive pass completions with 23 total on December 16, 2019 vs. the Indianapolis Colts and December 22, 2019 vs. the Tennessee Titans.

   a. True
   b. False

13. Darren Sharper holds the New Orleans Saints single game record for longest interception return at _____ yards on October 4, 2009 vs. the New York Jets.

   a. 89
   b. 95
   c. 99
   d. 101

14. The largest margin of victory in New Orleans Saints history was on October 23, 2011 vs. the _____ when the Saints won 62-7.

   a. Indianapolis Colts
   b. Carolina Panthers
   c. Tampa Bay Buccaneers
   d. Seattle Seahawks

15. Sammy Knight holds the New Orleans Saints record for most single game interceptions with _____ total on September 9, 2001 vs. the Buffalo Bills.

   a. 2
   b. 3
   c. 5
   d. 7

16. Reggie Bush and Joe Horn are tied for the New Orleans Saints record for most total touchdowns in a game. How many total touchdowns did they each record?

    a. 3
    b. 4
    c. 6
    d. 8

17. Wil Lutz holds the single season New Orleans Saints record for most field goals made with 32 total in 2019.

    a. True
    b. False

18. Morten Anderson holds the New Orleans Saints record for most career points with _____ total.

    a. 1,018
    b. 1,118
    c. 1,218
    d. 1,318

19. Michael Lewis holds the New Orleans Saints career record for most kickoff return yards with _____ total.

    a. 5,603
    b. 5,803
    c. 5,903
    d. d.6,053

20. Tom Dempsey holds the New Orleans Saints single game record for longest field goal at 63 yards on November 8, 1970 vs. the Detroit Lions.

a. True
b. False

QUIZ ANSWERS

1. B – 72

2. A - True

3. C – 50

4. C – 547

5. D – 8, 352

6. B – 40

7. A – True

8. D – 149

9. C – 389

10. B – 37

11. A – 123

12. A – True

13. C – 99

14. A – Indianapolis Colts

15. B – 3

16. B – 4

17. A – True

18. D – 1,318

19. C – 5,903

20. A – True

DID YOU KNOW?

1. The team the New Orleans Saints have beat the most times is the Atlanta Falcons (currently 49 times). The Atlanta Falcons are also the team they have lost to the most times (currently 52 times).

2. Tom Dempsey holds the New Orleans Saints single game record for most field goals with 6 total on November 16, 1969 vs. the New York Giants.

3. John Kasay holds the New Orleans Saints single season record for most points with 147 in 2011. Morten Anderson holds the New Orleans Saints career record for most points with 1, 318 total.

4. Drew Brees holds the New Orleans Saints and NFL record for most pass completions in a single season with 471 total in 2016.

5. Dave Whitsell holds the New Orleans Saints single season record for most passes intercepted with 10 total in 1967.

6. Dalton Hilliard and Alvin Kamara are tied for the New Orleans Saints single season record for most touchdown scored with 18 total each, Hilliard in 1989 and Kamara in 2018.

7. Reggie Bush holds the New Orleans Saints career record for most punt return touchdowns with 4 total.

8. Drew Brees holds the New Orleans Saints career record for most pass completions with 5,742 total (so far).

9. Pat Swilling and La'Roi Glover are tied for the New Orleans Saints single season record for most quarterback sacks with 17 total each, Swilling in 1991 and Glover in 2000.

10. Tom Myers holds the New Orleans Saints career record for most pass interception return yards with 621 yards total.

CHAPTER 7:

THE TRADE MARKET

QUIZ TIME!

1. On March 10, 2015 the New Orleans Saints traded _____ with a 4th round draft pick to the Seattle Seahawks in exchange for a 1st round pick (Stephone Anthony) and Max Unger.

   a. Mark Ingram
   b. Marques Colston
   c. Jimmy Graham
   d. Thomas Morstead

2. On March 27, 2002 the New Orleans Saints traded _____ to the Kansas City Chiefs in exchange for a 2003 3rd round draft pick (Wade Smith).

   a. Aaron Brooks
   b. Ricky Williams
   c. Deuce McAllister
   d. Willie Roaf

3. On March 8, 2002 the New Orleans Saints traded Ricky Williams with a 4th round draft pick to the Miami Dolphins in exchange for a 2002 1st round draft pick, a 2002 4th round draft pick and a 2003 1st draft pick.

    a. True

    b. False

4. On March 13, 2014 the New Orleans Saints traded Darren Sproles to the _____ in exchange for a 5th round draft pick (Ronald Powell).

    a. San Diego Chargers

    b. Philadelphia Eagles

    c. Cleveland Browns

    d. Miami Dolphins

5. On July 28, 2011 the New Orleans Saints traded Reggie Bush to the Miami Dolphins.

    a. True

    b. False

6. On March 13, 2015 the New Orleans Saints traded _____ to the Miami Dolphins for a2015 3rd round draft pick (P.J. Williams) and Dannell Ellerbe.

    a. Pierre Thomas

    b. Nick Toon

    c. Mark Ingram

    d. Kenny Stills

7. On May 9, 2014 the _____ traded Brandin Cooks (as a 2014 1st round draft pick) to the New Orleans

Saints in exchange for 2014 1st round draft pick and a 2014 3rd round draft pick.

   a. Los Angeles Rams

   b. New England Patriots

   c. Arizona Cardinals

   d. Houston Texans

8. On March 10, 2017 the New Orleans Saints traded Brandin Cooks and a 2017 4th round draft pick to the _____ in exchange for Ryan Ramczyk (as a 1st round draft pick) and a 3rd round draft pick (Trey Hendrickson).

   a. New England Patriots

   b. Los Angeles Rams

   c. Houston Texans

   d. Arizona Cardinals

9. On April 6, 2009 the New Orleans Saints traded a 7th round draft pick (Pat McAfee) and a 2010 5th round pick (Reshad Jones) to the _____ in exchange for a 5th round draft pick (Thomas Morstead).

   a. Indianapolis Colts

   b. Philadelphia Eagles

   c. Miami Dolphins

   d. Atlanta Falcons

10. On October 10, 2017 the New Orleans Saints traded Adrian Peterson to the Arizona Cardinals in exchange for a 6th round draft pick.

   a. True

   b. False

11. On April 28, 2011 the New Orleans Saints traded a 2nd round draft pick (Shane Vereen) and a 2012 1st round draft pick (Kevin Zeitler) to the _____ in exchange for a 1st round draft pick (Mark Ingram).

    a. New York Giants
    b. Cleveland Browns
    c. New England Patriots
    d. Cincinnati Bengals

12. On April 26, 2013 the New Orleans Saints traded Chris Ivory to the New York Giants for a 4th round draft pick (Don Sims).

    a. True
    b. False

13. On April 28, 2017 the New Orleans Saints traded 7th round draft pick (Adrian Colbert) and a 2018 2nd round draft pick (Derrius Guice) to the _____ in exchange for a 3rd round draft pick (Alvin Kamara).

    a. Washington Redskins
    b. Miami Dolphins
    c. San Francisco 49ers
    d. New York Giants

14. On April 26, 2018 the New Orleans Saints traded 1st round draft pick (Rashaad Penny) and a 5th round draft pick (Micah Kiser) and a 2019 1st round draft pick (Deandre Baker) to the Green Bay Packers in exchange for a 1st round draft pick (Marcus Davenport).

a. True

b. False

15. On September 2, 2019 the New Orleans Saints traded _____ to the Miami Dolphins in exchange for Kiko Alonso.

    a. Manti Te'o

    b. Zach Line

    c. Eli Apple

    d. Vince Biegel

16. On April 27, 2019 the New Orleans Saints traded 4th round draft pick (Amani Hooker) and 5th round draft pick (D'Andre Walker) to the _____ in exchange for a 4th round draft pick (Chauncey Gardner-Johnson).

    a. Tennessee Titans

    b. New York Jets

    c. Seattle Seahawks

    d. Dallas Cowboys

17. On February 29, 2008 the New Orleans Saints traded a 4th round draft pick to the New York Jets in exchange for _____.

    a. Jonathan Vilma

    b. Deuce McAllister

    c. Marques Colston

    d. Pierre Thomas

18. On April 3, 2007 the New Orleans Saints traded a 6th round draft pick to the Miami Dolphins in exchange for

    _____.

    a. Devery Henderson
    b. Steve Weatherford
    c. Olindo Mare
    d. Jahri Evans

19. On April 30, 2006 the New Orleans Saints traded a 4th round draft pick (Max Jean-Giles) to the Philadelphia Eagles in exchange for Hollis Thomas and a 4th round draft pick (_____).

    a. Deuce McAllister
    b. Will Smith
    c. Devery Henderson
    d. Jahri Evans

20. On April 25, 2020 the New Orleans Saints traded a 2021 6th round draft pick to the Houston Texans in exchange for a 2020 7th round draft pick (Tommy Stevens).

    a. True
    b. False

QUIZ ANSWERS

1. C – Jimmy Graham

2. D – Willie Roaf

3. A – True

4. B – Philadelphia Eagles

5. True

6. D – Kenny Stills

7. C – Arizona Cardinals

8. A – New England Patriots

9. B – Philadelphia Eagles

10. A – True

11. C – New England Patriots

12. B – False, New York Jets

13. C – San Francisco 49ers

14. A – True

15. D – Vince Biegel

16. B – New York Jets

17. A – Jonathan Vilma

18. C – Olindo Mare

19. D – Jahri Evans

20. A – True

DID YOU KNOW?

1. On August 29, 2018 the New Orleans Saints traded a 2019 3rd round draft pick (Miles Boykin) to the New York Jets in exchange for Teddy Bridgewater and a 2019 6th round draft pick (Saquan Hampton).

2. On August 26, 2013 the New Orleans Saints traded a 2014 7th round draft pick (Corey Nelson) to the San Francisco 49ers in exchange for Parys Haralson.

3. 3 On August 21, 2012 the New Orleans Saints traded a 2013 7th round draft pick (Ryan Seymour) to the Seattle Seahawks in exchange for Barrett Rudd.

4. On June 21, 2010 the New Orleans Saints traded Jammal Brown and a 2011 5th round draft pick (Niles Paul) to the Washington Redskins in exchange for a 2011 3rd round draft pick (Martez Wilson).

5. On September 5, 2009 the New Orleans Saints traded a 2011 6th round pick (Mike Mohamed) to the New England Patriots in exchange for David Thomas.

6. On July 1, 2008 the New Orleans Saints traded an undisclosed draft pick to the New York Giants in exchange for Jeremy Shockey.

7. On April 6, 2006 the New Orleans Saints traded Wayne Grandy to the Atlanta Falcons in exchange for Bryan Scott.

8. On April 24, 2004 the New Orleans Saints a 2nd round draft

pick (Dontarrious Thomas) to the Minnesota Vikings in exchange for a 2nd round draft pick (Devery Henderson) and a 5th round draft pick (Mark Wilson).

9. On September 1, 2002 the New Orleans Saints traded Ricky Williams to the Indianapolis Colts in exchange for a 2003 7th round draft pick (Tully Banta-Cain).

10. On March 5, 1998 the New Orleans Saints traded Eric Allen to the Oakland Raiders in exchange for a 4th round draft pick (Fred Weary).

CHAPTER 8:

DRAFT DAY

QUIZ TIME!

1. With the 32th overall pick in the 2nd round of the 2001 NFL Draft, the _____ selected Drew Brees.

   a. New Orleans Saints
   b. San Diego Chargers
   c. San Francisco 49ers
   d. Green Bay Packers

2. With the 2nd overall pick in the 1st round of the _____ NFL Draft, the New Orleans selected Archie Manning (yes, Eli and Peyton's dad).

   a. 1969
   b. 1970
   c. 1971
   d. 1972

3. With the 2nd overall pick in the 1st round of the _____ NFL Draft, the New Orleans Saints selected Reggie Bush.

   a. 2004
   b. 2006

c. 2007

d. 2009

4. With the 23rd overall pick in 1st round of the _____ NFL draft, the New Orleans Saints selected Deuce McAllister.

   a. 1997

   b. 1999

   c. 2000

   d. 2001

5. With the 86th overall pick in the 4th round of the _____ NFL draft, the New Orleans Saints selected Morten Anderson.

   a. 1980

   b. 1981

   c. 1982

   d. 1984

6. With the 252nd overall pick in the ____ round of the 2006 NFL Draft, the New Orleans Saints selected Marques Colston.

   a. 3rd

   b. 5th

   c. 6th

   d. 7th

7. With the 67th overall pick in the 3rd round of the 2017 NFL Draft, the New Orelans Saints selected Alvin Kamara.

   a. True

   b. False

8. With the _____ overall pick in the 2nd round of the 1981 NFL Draft, the New Orleans Saints selected Rickey Jackson.

    a. 50th

    b. 51st

    c. 55th

    d. 62nd

9. With the 12th overall pick in the 1st round of the _____ NFL Draft, the New Orleans Saints selected Stan Brock.

    a. 1976

    b. 1979

    c. 1980

    d. 1983

10. The New Orleans Saints drafted Cameron Jordan in the 1st round, 24th overall in the 2011 NFL Draft.

    a. True

    b. False

11. With the 8th overall pick in the 1st round of the 1993 NFL Draft, the New Orleans Saints selected _____.

    a. Wade Wilson

    b. Derek Brown

    c. Brad Muster

    d. Willie Roaf

12. Jimmy Graham was drafted in the 3rd round, 95th overall of the 2010 NFL Draft by the New Orleans Saints.

    a. True

    b. False

13. With the 60th overall pick in the 3rd round of the 1986 NFL Draft, the New Orleans Saints selected _____.

    a. Dave Wilson
    b. Dave Waymer
    c. Pat Swilling
    d. Reuben Mayes

14. In the 1st round of the 2010 NFL Draft, the New Orleans Saints selected _____, 19th overall.

    a. Bobby Hebert
    b. Craig Heyward
    c. Dalton Hilliard
    d. Wayne Martin

15. With the 28th overall pick in the 1st round of the 2011 NFL Draft, the New Orleans Saints selected _____.

    a. Mark Ingram
    b. Pierre Thomas
    c. Devery Henderson
    d. Will Smith

16. With the 3rd overall pick in the 1st round of the 1986 NFL Draft, the _____ selected Jim Everett.

    a. Los Angeles Rams
    b. Houston Oilers
    c. San Diego Chargers
    d. New York Giants

17. With the 131st overall pick in the 4th round of the 1999 NFL Draft, the _____ selected Aaron Brooks.

a. Minnesota Vikings

b. Dallas Cowboys

c. Oakland Raiders

d. Green Bay Packers

18. Latavius Murray was drafted in the 6th round, 181st overall in the 2013 NFL Draft by the _____.

a. Minnesota Vikings

b. Oakland Raiders

c. Miami Dolphins

d. Jacksonville Jaguars

19. With the 77th overall pick in the 3rd round of the 2012 NFL Draft, the _____ selected Demario Davis.

a. Cleveland Browns

b. Chicago Bears

c. New York Jets

d. Atlanta Falcons

20. Ricky Williams was selected by the New Orleans Saints in the 1st round, 5th overall in the 1999 NFL Draft.

a. True

b. False

QUIZ ANSWERS

1. B – San Diego Chargers

2. C – 1971

3. B – 2006

4. D – 2001

5. C – 1982

6. D – 7th

7. A – True

8. B – 51st

9. C – 1980

10. A – True

11. D – Willie Roaf

12. A – True

13. C – Pat Swilling

14. D – Wayne Martin

15. A – Mark Ingram

16. B – Houston Oilers

17. D – Green Bay Packers

18. B – Oakland Raiders

19. C – New York Jets

20. A – True

DID YOU KNOW?

1. Jahri Evans was selected by the New Orleans Saints in the 4th round, 108th overall in the 2006 NFL Draft.

2. Chuck Muncie was selected by the New Orleans Saints in the 1st round, 3rd overall in the 1976 NFL Draft.

3. Thomas Morstead was selected by the New Orleans Saints in the 5th round, 164th overall in the 2009 NFL Draft.

4. Tom Myers was selected by the New Orleans Saints in the 3rd round, 74th overall in the 1972 NFL Draft.

5. Dalton Hilliard was selected by the New Orleans Saints in the 2nd round, 31st overall in the 1986 NFL Draft.

6. Devery Henderson was selected by the New Orleans Saints in the 2nd round, 50th overall in the 2004 NFL Draft.

7. Malcolm Jenkins was selected by the New Orleans Saints in the 1st round, 14th overall in the 2009 NFL Draft.

8. Chauncey Gardner-Johnson was selected by the New Orleans Saints in the 4th round, 105th overall in the 2019 NFL Draft.

9. Jared Cook was selected by the Tennessee Titans in the 3rd round, 89th overall in the 2009 NFL Draft.

10. Emmanuel Sanders was selected by the Pittsburgh Steelers in the 3rd round, 82nd overall in the 2010 NFL Draft.

CHAPTER 9:

ODDS & ENDS

QUIZ TIME!

1. Which celebrity did Reggie Bush once date?

   a. Katy Perry

   b. Rihanna

   c. Jennifer Lopez

   d. Kim Kardashian

2. Peyton and Eli Manning are Archie Manning's sons.

   a. True

   b. False

3. Deuce McAllister once owned a _____ car dealership in Jackson, Mississippi.

   a. Ford

   b. Nissan

   c. Chevrolet

   d. Kia

4. From 2001 to 2004 Pat Swilling served as a member of the _____ House of Representatives.

    a. Georgia
    b. California
    c. Louisiana
    d. Michigan

5. Before the start of every home game, the Carolina Panthers have a guest bang their "Keep Pounding" drum. This is in honor of _____ and his "Keep Pounding" speech after his cancer diagnosis.

    a. Sam Mills
    b. Joe Horn
    c. Morten Andersen
    d. George Rogers

6. 6. Sean Payton began his coaching career as an offensive assistant at _____.

    a. San Jose State University
    b. UC Berkeley
    c. San Diego State University
    d. UC San Diego

7. 7. Willie Roaf's mom, Andree Layton Roaf was the first black woman to serve on the Arkansas Supreme Court.

    a. True
    b. False

8. Pierre Thomas' iCan Foundation fights against _____.

a. Childhood Cancer

b. Childhood Obesity

c. Mental Health Stigmas

d. Teen Drug Use

9. Which reality TV show did Drew Brees appear on in 2015?

a. Below Deck

b. The Amazing Race

c. Running Wild with Bear Grylls

d. Top Chef

10. Ricky Williams is a certified _____.

a. Esthetician

b. Dietician

c. Dog Trainer

d. Yoga Instructor

11. In 2019, Ricky Williams was the runner up on which TV reality show?

a. Survivor

b. Celebrity Big Brother

c. The Amazing Race

d. The Bachelorette

12. Rueben Mayes is one of only five Saskatchewan natives to make it to the NFL.

a. True

b. False

13. Cameron Jordan's father, Steve Jordan was an NFL tight end and spent 13 seasons with the _____.

a. New Orleans Saints

b. San Francisco 49ers

c. Minnesota Vikings

d. Oakland Raiders

14. Archie Manning owns a football-themed restaurant called
_____.

a. Manning Bros

b. Manning's

c. Hail Mary's

d. Touchdown Grill

15. Pat Swilling is currently a _____ in New Orleans.

a. Sports Psychiologist

b. Personal Trainer

c. Landscaper

d. Real Estate Developer

16. Aaron Brooks is the second cousin of Michael Vick.

a. True

b. False

17. In February 2008, Drew Brees signed a promotional deal with _____ to promote their new line of burgers.

a. Red Robin

b. Chili's Grill and Bar

c. Shake Shack

d. Applebee's

18. In high school, Jonathan Vilma was teammates with
_____.

    a. Aaron Rodgers
    b. Cam Newton
    c. Frank Gore
    d. Russell Wilson

19. During his sophomore season, _____ won
the first Heisman Trophy ever awarded to an Alabama
Crimson Tide player.

    a. Vinnie Sunseri
    b. Alvin Kamara
    c. Ken Stabler
    d. Mark Ingram

20. Morten Andersen holds the NFL record for games played
at 382 total.

    a. True
    b. False

QUIZ ANSWERS

1. D – Kim Kardashian

2. A – True

3. B – Nissan

4. C – Louisiana

5. A – Sam Mills

6. C – San Diego State University

7. A – True

8. B – Childhood Obesity

9. C – Running Wild with Bear Grylls

10. D – Yoga Instructor

11. B – Celebrity Big Brother

12. A – True

13. C – Minnesota Vikings

14. B – Manning's

15. D – Real Estate Developer

16. A – True

17. B – Chili's Bar & Grill

18. C – Frank Gore

19. D – Mark Ingram

20. A – True

DID YOU KNOW?

1. In a film named *Gleason,* Steve Gleason's struggle with having Lou Gehrig's disease is chronicled.

2. Will Smith was shot and killed during an altercation in New Orleans after an alcohol involved car accident.

3. La'Roi Glover is currently the Assistant Defensive Line Coach for the Los Angeles Rams.

4. Willie Roaf's sister, Phoebe is the Episcopal Bishop for the Diocese of West Tennessee.

5. In 2018, Alvin Kamara became the first NFL player to reach 1,000 rushing yards and 1,000 receiving yards in his first 20 career games.

6. In 2017, Ricky Williams was on *The New Celebrity Apprentice* and finished in 7th place.

7. Thomas Morstead and his wife, Lauren, created the charity What You Give Will Grow in 2014. The organization has given over $2,500,000 to various causes

8. After becoming a single father at 21 years old, Jabari Greer created a non-profit foundation, the Greer Campaign, focused on programs to assist both single and married fathers in developing their parenting skills.

9. In 2010, San Diego State University Athletics inducted La'Roi Glover to the Aztec Hall of Fame. At that point in time, Glover ranked third all-time at San Diego State with 44.5 tackles for loss and fourth all-time in sacks.

10. Problems with cocaine forced Chuck Munice into early retirement. After going to prison, Muncie created the Chuck Munice Youth Foundation to help turn others' lives around through mentoring programs.

CHAPTER 10:

OFFENSE

QUIZ TIME!

1. How many Pro Bowls was Deuce McAllister named to over the course of his 8-season NFL career?

   a. 0

   b. 2

   c. 3

   d. 5

2. Marques Colston played his entire 10-season NFL career with the New Orleans Saints.

   a. True

   b. False

3. Over the course of his 15-season NFL career, Archie Manning played for the New Orleans Saints, Houston Oilers and the _____.

   a. San Francisco 49ers

   b. Indianapolis Colts

   c. Green Bay Packers

   d. Minnesota Vikings

4. Jimmy Graham won a Super Bowl Championship during his time with the New Orleans Saints.

    a. True
    b. False

5. What year was Ken Stabler inducted into the Pro Football Hall of Fame?

    a. 2012
    b. 2014
    c. 2016
    d. 2018

6. How many touchdowns did Reggie Bush record during his 2006 season with the New Orleans Saints?

    a. 4
    b. 6
    c. 9
    d. 11

7. Devery Henderson played his entire 9-season NFL career with the New Orleans Saints.

    a. True
    b. False

8. So far in his career, Mark Ingram has played for the New Orleans Saints and the _____.

    a. Arizona Cardinals
    b. Pittsburgh Steelers
    c. Chicago Bears
    d. Baltimore Ravens

9. How many seasons total did Pierre Thomas play for the New Orleans Saints?

    a. 5

    b. 7

    c. 8

    d. 11

10. Which of the following teams did former Saint, Reggie Bush NOT play for over the course of his 11-season NFL career?

    a. Philadelphia Eagles

    b. San Francisco 49ers

    c. Miami Dolphins

    d. Detroit Lions

11. How many Super Bowls did Archie Manning win over the course of his 15-season NFL career?

    a. 0

    b. 1

    c. 3

    d. 4

12. Over the course of his 12-season NFL career, Jim Everett played for the New Orleans Saints, Los Angeles Rams and the San Diego Chargers.

    a. True

    b. False

13. How many Pro Bowls was Chuck Muncie named to over the course of his 10-season NFL career?

a. 1

b. 2

c. 3

d. 5

14. How many Super Bowl Championships did Darren Sproles win over the course of his 14-season NFL career?

a. 0

b. 1

c. 2

d. 3

15. How many total seasons did Tony Galbreath play for the New Orleans Saints?

a. 3

b. 4

c. 5

d. 6

16. Which of the following teams did former Saint Courtney Roby NOT play for over the course of his 9-season NFL career?

a. Tennessee Titans

b. Carolina Panthers

c. Atlanta Falcons

d. Indianapolis Colts

17. So far in his 20-season NFL career, Drew Brees has played for the New Orleans Saints and the _____.

a. San Diego Chargers

b. Arizona Cardinals

c. San Francisco 49ers

d. Oakland Raiders

18. How many Pro Bowls has Jimmy Graham been named to so far in his career (as of the end of the 2019 season)?

    a. 3

    b. 5

    c. 7

    d. 9

19. How many Pro Bowls was Bobby Hebert named to over the course of his 11-season NFL career?

    a. 0

    b. 1

    c. 3

    d. 6

20. Lorenzo Neal was named to 4 Pro Bowls over the course of his 16-season NFL career.

    a. True

    b. False

QUIZ ANSWERS

1. B – 2

2. A – True

3. D – Minnesota Vikings

4. B – False, He joined the Saints in 2010

5. C – 2016

6. B – 6

7. A – True

8. D – Baltimore Ravens

9. C – 8

10. A – Philadelphia Eagles

11. A – 0

12. A – True

13. C – 3

14. B – 1

15. C – 5

16. B – Carolina Panthers

17. A – San Diego Chargers

18. B – 5

19. B – 1

20. A – True

DID YOU KNOW?

1. Quarterback Drew Brees is in his 15th season with the New Orleans Saints. He also spent 5 seasons with the San Diego Chargers. So far, he has been named to 13 Pro Bowls, is a 1x All-Pro, 1x Super Bowl Champion, 2004 AP Comeback Player of the Year Award winner, 2006 Walter Payton Man of the Year Award winner, 2008 AP Offensive Player of the Year Award winner, 2009 Bert Bell Award winner and 2011 AP Offensive Player of the Year Award.

2. Archie Manning played 11 seasons of his NFL career with the New Orleans Saints He also played for the Houston Oilers and Minnesota Vikings. He is a 2x Pro Bowler and his sons, Peyton and Eli went on to become NFL quarterbacks as well.

3. Deuce McAllister played his entire 8-season NFL career with the New Orleans Saints. He is a 2x Pro Bowler.

4. Marques Colston played his entire 10-season NFL career with the New Orleans Saints. He is a 1x Super Bowl Champion.

5. Reggie Bush played 5 seasons of his NFL career with the New Orleans Saints. He also played for the San Francisco 49ers, Detroit Lions, Miami Dolphins, Buffalo Bills. He is a 1x Super Bowl Champion.

6. Devery Henderson played his entire 9-season NFL career

with the New Orleans Saints. He is a 1x Super Bowl
Champion.

7. Jimmy Graham played 5 seasons of his NFL career with
   the New Orleans Saints. So far in his career, he has also
   played for the Seattle Seahawks and the Green Bay
   Packers. He currently plays for the Chicago Bears. He is a
   5x Pro Bowler and 1x All-Pro.

8. Dalton Hilliard played his entire 8 season NFL career with
   the New Orleans Saints. He was a 1x Pro Bowler.

9. Jim Everett played 3 seasons of his NFL career with the
   New Orleans Saints. He also played for the Los Angeles
   Rams and San Diego Chargers. He was a 1x Pro Bowler.

10. Pierre Thomas played 8 seasons of his NFL career with the
    New Orleans Saints. He also played for the San Francisco
    49ers and Washington Redskins. He is a 1x Super Bowl
    Champion.

CHAPTER 11:

DEFENSE

QUIZ TIME!

1. Over the course of his 12-season NFL career, Pat Swilling played for the New Orleans Saints, Detroit Lions and the

    _____.

    a. Green Bay Packers
    b. Arizona Cardinals
    c. San Francisco 49ers
    d. Oakland Raiders.

2. Malcolm Jenkins has played his entire 12-season NFL career with the New Orleans Saints.

    a. True
    b. False

3. How many Pro Bowls was Darren Sharper named to over the course of his 14-season NFL career?

    a. 3
    b. 4
    c. 5
    d. 7

4. Over the course of his 12-season NFL career, Sam Mills played for the New Orleans Saints and the _____.

    a. Carolina Panthers

    b. Atlanta Falcons

    c. New York Jets

    d. New England Patriots

5. How many seasons did Manti Te'o play for the New Orleans Saints?

    a. 1

    b. 2

    c. 3

    d. 4

6. How many Super Bowl Championships did Jabari Greer win over the course of his 10-season NFL career??

    a. 0

    b. 1

    c. 2

    d. 3

7. Will Smith played his entire 9-season NFL career with the New Orleans Saints.

    a. True

    b. False

8. Which of the following teams did former Saint La'Roi Glover NOT play for over the course of his 13-season NFL career?

    a. Oakland Raiders

    b. Dallas Cowboys

c. San Francisco 49ers

d. St. Louis Rams

9. Over the course of his 11-season NFL career, Roman Harper played for the New Orleans Saints and the

    _____.

    a. Tampa Bay Buccaneers

    b. Carolina Panthers

    c. Denver Broncos

    d. Cincinnati Bengals

10. Over the course of his 12-season NFL career, how many times was Sammy Knight named to the Pro Bowl?

    a. 1

    b. 2

    c. 4

    d. 5

11. What year was Rickey Jackson inducted into the Pro Football Hall of Fame?

    a. 2007

    b. 2008

    c. 2009

    d. 2010

12. Rickey Jackson played his entire 12-season NFL career with the New Orleans Saints.

    a. True

    b. False

13. How many Pro Bowls was Jonathan Vilma named to over the course of his 10-season NFL career?

    a. 2
    b. 3
    c. 5
    d. 7

14. Which of the following teams did former Saint Scott Fujita NOT play for over the course of his 11-season NFL career?

    a. Cleveland Browns
    b. Kansas City Chiefs
    c. Houston Texans
    d. Dallas Cowboys

15. How many seasons did Gene Atkins play for the New Orleans Saints?

    a. 4
    b. 5
    c. 7
    d. 9

16. Charles Grant won a Super Bowl Championship with the New Orleans Saints.

    a. True
    b. False

17. How many seasons did Sam Mills play for the New Orleans Saints?

    a. 06
    b. 7

c. 8

d. 9

18. Over the course of his 15-season NFL career, Rickey Jackson was named to _____ Pro Bowls.

    a. 1

    b. 3

    c. 6

    d. 7

19. How many Super Bowl Championships did Darren Sharper win over the course of his 14-season NFL career?

    a. 0

    b. 1

    c. 2

    d. 3

20. Pat Swilling was named the 1991 AP Defensive Player of the Year.

    a. True

    b. False

QUIZ ANSWERS

1. D – Oakland Raiders

2. B – False, Saints and Philadelphia Eagles

3. C – 5

4. A – Carolina Panthers

5. C – 3

6. B – 1

7. A – True

8. C – San Francisco 49ers

9. B – Carolina Panthers

10. A – 1

11. D – 2010

12. B – False, Saints and San Francisco 49ers

13. B – 3

14. C – Houston Texans

15. C – 7

16. A – True

17. D – 9

18. C – 6

19. B – 1

20. A – True

DID YOU KNOW?

1. Rickey Jackson spent 13 seasons of his NFL career with the New Orleans Saints. He also played for the San Francisco 49ers. He is a member of the Pro Football Hall of Fame, a 6x Pro Bowler and 1x Super Bowl Champion.

2. Pat Swilling spent 7 seasons of his NFL career with the New Orleans Saints. He also played for the Oakland Raiders and Detroit Lions. He is a 5x Pro Bowler, 2x All-Pro and the 1991 AP Defensive Player of the Year Award winner.

3. Sam Mills spent 9 seasons of his NFL career with the New Orleans Saints. He also played for the Carolina Panthers. He is a 5x Pro Bowler and 1x All-Pro.

4. Will Smith spent his entire 9-season NFL career with the New Orleans Saints. He is a 1x Pro Bowler and 1x Super Bowl Champion.

5. La'Roi Glover spent 5 seasons of his NFL career with the New Orleans Saints. He also played for the Oakland Raiders, Dallas Cowboys and St. Louis Rams. He is a 1x Pro Bowler, 1x All-Pro and member of the HOF All- 2000's Team.

6. Darren Sharper spent the final two seasons of his NFL career with the New Orleans Saints. He also played for the Green Bay Packers and Minnesota Vikings. He is a 5x Pro

Bowler, 2x All-Pro, 1x Super Bowl Champion and member of the HOF All-2000's Team.

7. Jonathan Vilma spent 6 seasons of his NFL career with the New Orleans Saints. He also played for the New York Jets. He is a 3x Pro Bowler, 1x Super Bowl Champion and the 2004 AP Defensive Rookie of the Year Award winner.

8. Malcolm Jenkins currently plays for the New Orleans Saints. He spent 5 seasons with the Saints before playing for the Philadelphia Eagles for 6 seasons, then returning to New Orleans. So far in his career, he is a 3x Pro Bowler and 2x Super Bowl Champion.

9. Sammy Knight spent 6 seasons of his NFL career with the New Orleans Saints. He also played for the Miami Dolphins, Jacksonville Jaguars, New York Giants and Kansas City Chiefs. He is a 1x Pro Bowler.

10. Scott Fujita spent 4 seasons of his NFL career with the New Orleans Saints. He also played for the Cleveland Browns, Kansas City Chiefs and Dallas Cowboys. He is a 1x Super Bowl Champion.

CHAPTER 12:

SPECIAL TEAMS

QUIZ TIME!

1. What year was Morten Andersen inducted into the Pro Football Hall of Fame?

    a. 2015

    b. 2016

    c. 2017

    d. 2018

2. Morten Andersen did NOT win a Super Bowl Championship in his 25-season NFL career.

    a. True

    b. False

3. How many Pro Bowls was Morten Andersen named to over the course of his 25-season NFL career?

    a. 6

    b. 7

    c. 8

    d. 9

4. Which of the following teams did Morten Andersen NOT play for over the course of his 25-season NFL career?

    a. Atlanta Falcons

    b. Minnesota Vikings

    c. New York Giants

    d. Denver Broncos

5. How many Pro Bowls has current Saint, Thomas Morstead been named to so far in his career (as of the end of the 2019 season)?

    a. 0

    b. 1

    c. 2

    d. 3

6. How many Pro Bowls has current Saint, Wil Lutz been named to so far in his career (as of the end of the 2019 season)?

    a. 0

    b. 1

    c. 2

    d. 3

7. Over the course of his 20-season NFL career, John Kasay played for the New Orleans Saints, Seattle Seahawks and Carolina Panthers.

    a. True

    b. False

8. Which of the following teams did former Saint, Olindo Mare NOT play for over the course of his 16-season NFL career?

    a. Seattle Seahawks
    b. Green Bay Packers
    c. Miami Dolphins
    d. Chicago Bears

9. How many Pro Bowls was Tom Dempsey named to over the course of his 11-season NFL career?

    a. 0
    b. 1
    c. 2
    d. 3

10. How many Pro Bowls was John Carney named to over the course of his 25-season NFL career?

    a. 0
    b. 1
    c. 2
    d. 3

11. How many seasons did Garrett Hartley play for the New Orleans Saints?

    a. 2
    b. 3
    c. 4
    d. 5

12. John Kasay was drafted by the Seattle Seahawks.

    a. True
    b. False

13. How many Super Bowl Championships did Tom Blanchard win over the course of his 11-season NFL career?

    a. 0
    b. 1
    c. 2
    d. 3

14. Which of the following teams did former Saint, Shayne Graham NOT play for over the course of his 17-season NFL career?

    a. New England Patriots
    b. Cincinnati Bengals
    c. New York Jets
    d. Baltimore Ravens

15. Which of the following teams did former Saint, Billy Cundiff NOT play for over the course of his 13-season NFL career?

    a. Dallas Cowboys
    b. Cleveland Browns
    c. Buffalo Bills
    d. Kansas City Chiefs

16. Wil Lutz has played in all 16 games every season for the New Orleans Saints from 2016-2019.

a. True

b. False

17. How many seasons did Doug Brien play for the New Orleans Saints?

    a. 5

    b. 6

    c. 7

    d. 8

18. How many Super Bowl championships did former Saint, Garo Yepremian win over the course of his 14-season NFL career?

    a. 0

    b. 1

    c. 2

    d. 3

19. How many seasons did Steve Weatherford play for the New Orleans Saints?

    a. 3

    b. 4

    c. 5

    d. 6

20. Over the course of his 11-season NFL career, Tom Blanchard played for the New Orleans Saints, New York Giants and Tampa Bay Buccaneers.

    a. True

    b. False

QUIZ ANSWERS

1. C – 2017

2. True

3. B – 7

4. D – Denver Broncos

5. B – 1

6. B – 1

7. A – True

8. B – Green Bay Packers

9. B – 1

10. C – 3

11. D – 5

12. A – True

13. A – 0

14. C – New York Jets

15. D – Kansas City Chiefs

16. A – True

17. B – 6

18. C – 2

19. A – 3

20. A – True

DID YOU KNOW?

1. Morten Andersen spent 13 seasons of his NFL career with the New Orleans Saints. He also played for the Atlanta Falcons, Kansas City Chiefs, Minnesota Vikings and New York Giants. He is a member of the Pro Football Hall of Fame, a 7x Pro Bowler, 3x All-Pro, and member of the HOF All-1980's Team and the HOF All-1990's Team.

2. Current Saint, Thomas Morstead has been with the team since 2009. He has played his entire NFL career in New Orleans so far. He is a 1x Pro Bowler and a 1x Super Bowl Champion.

3. Current Saint, Wil Lutz has been with the team since 2016. He has played his entire NFL career in New Orleans so far. He is a 1x Pro Bowler.

4. John Carney spent 8 seasons of his NFL career with the New Orleans Saints. He also played for the San Diego Chargers, Tampa Bay Buccaneers, Jacksonville Jaguars, Kansas City Chiefs, New York Giants and Los Angeles Rams. He is a 2x Pro Bowler, 1x All-Pro and 1x Super Bowl Champion.

5. John Kasay spent his final season in the NFL with the New Orleans Saints. He also played for the Carolina Panthers and Seattle Seahawks. He is a 1x Pro Bowler.

6. Olindo Mare spent one season of his NFL career with the New Orleans Saints. He also played for the Miami

Dolphins, Carolina Panthers, Chicago Bears and Seattle Seahawks. He is a 1x Pro Bowler and 1x All-Pro.

7. Tom Dempsey spent two seasons of his NFL career with the New Orleans Saints. He also played for the Philadelphia Eagles, Buffalo Bills, Los Angeles Rams, and Houston Oilers. He is a 1x Pro Bowler.

8. Garo Yepremian spent one season of his NFL career with the New Orleans Saints. He also played for the Miami Dolphins, Detroit Lions and Tampa Bay Buccaneers. He was a 2x Pro Bowler, 2x All-Pro, 2x Super Bowl Champion and member of the HOF All-1970's Team.

9. Shayne Graham spent one season of his NFL career with the New Orleans Saints. He also played for the Cincinnati Bengals, Atlanta Falcons, Baltimore Ravens, Buffalo Bills, Carolina Panthers, Houston Texans, Miami Dolphins, New England Patriots and New York Giants. He is a 1x Pro Bowler.

10. Doug Brein spent 6 seasons of his NFL career with the New Orleans Saints. He also played for the New York Jets, San Francisco 49ers, Chicago Bears, Indianapolis Colts, Minnesota Vikings and Tampa Bay Buccaneers. He is a 1x Super Bowl Champion.

CHAPTER 13:

SUPER BOWL

QUIZ TIME!

1. How many Super Bowls have the New Orleans Saints won in franchise history?

   a. 0

   b. 1

   c. 2

   d. 3

2. How many NFC Conference Championships have the New Orleans Saints won (as of the end of the 2019 season)?

   a. 0

   b. 1

   c. 2

   d. 3

3. Which team did the New Orleans Saints face in Super Bowl XLIV?

   a. Pittsburgh Steelers

   b. Indianapolis Colts

c. New England Patriots

d. Denver Broncos

4. Where was Super Bowl XLIV held?

a. University of Phoenix Stadium – Glendale, Arizona

b. Cowboys Stadium – Arlington, Texas

c. Levi's Stadium – Santa Clara, California

d. Sun Life Stadium – Miami Gardens, Florida

5. Who sang the National Anthem at Super Bowl XLIV?

a. Demi Lovato

b. Jennifer Hudson

c. Carrie Underwood

d. Kelly Clarkson

6. How many total appearances have the New Orleans Saints made in the NFL Playoffs (as of the end of the 2019 season)?

a. 10

b. 13

c. 17

d. 21

7. Drew Brees was named MVP of Super Bowl XLIV.

a. True

b. False

8. Who was a part of the ceremonial coin toss before Super Bowl XLIV?

a. Emmitt Smith

b. Warren Sapp

c. Don Shula

d. Curtis Martin

9. Who performed at the Super Bowl XLIV Halftime Show?

a. Justin Timberlake

b. Lady Gaga

c. The Who

d. Maroon 5

10. Who was the New Orleans Saints' head coach during Super Bowl XLIV?

a. Jim E. Mora

b. Jim Haslett

c. Bum Phillips

d. Sean Payton

11. Drew Brees' 32 completions in Super Bowl XLIV tied a Super Bowl record previously set by _____.

a. Aaron Rodgers

b. Tom Brady

c. Peyton Manning

d. Eli Manning

12. Held on Feburary 7, 2010, Super Bowl XLIV was the latest calendar date for a Super Bowl so far.

a. True

b. False

13. What was the final score of Super Bowl XLIV?

a. Saints 7 – Colts 0

b. Saints 21 – Colts 7

c. Saints 31 – Colts 17

d. Saints 41 – Colts 21

14. Super Bowl XLIV was broadcasted live on which TV network?

    a. FOX

    b. ABC

    c. NBC

    d. CBS

15. Who sang "America the Beautiful" at Super Bowl XLIV?

    a. Chris Daughtry

    b. Queen Latifah

    c. Kelly Clarkson

    d. Coldplay

16. The in-game attendance for Super Bowl XLIV was 74,059 total.

    a. True

    b. False

17. What was the game length for Super Bowl XLIV?

    a. 2 hours 59 minutes

    b. 3 hours 8 minutes

    c. 3 hours 14 minutes

    d. 3 hours 46 minutes

18. What was the temperature at kickoff for Super Bowl XLIV?

    a. 89° F

    b. 82° F

c. 77° F

d. 66° F

19. What time did kickoff occur for Super Bowl XLIV?

  a. 1:31 pm EST

  b. 3:48 pm EST

  c. 6:32 pm EST

  d. 7:05 pm EST

20. The New Orleans Saints were the last team to win a championship game of a major professional sports league in North America on their first attempt until the Toronto Raptors of the NBA in 2019.

  a. True

  b. False

QUIZ ANSWERS

1. B – 1 (2009)

2. B – 1 (2009)

3. B – Indianapolis Colts

4. D - Sun Life Stadium – Miami Gardens, Florida

5. C – Carrie Underwood

6. B – 13

7. A – True

8. A – Emmitt Smith

9. C – The Who

10. D – Sean Payton

11. B – Tom Brady

12. A - True

13. C – Saints 31 – Colts 17

14. D – CBS

15. B – Queen Latifah

16. A – True

17. C – 3 hours 14 minutes

18. D – 66° F

19. C – 6:32 pm EST

20. A – True

DID YOU KNOW?

1. Super Bowl XLIV was the last Super Bowl to have a uniquely designed logo.

2. Super Bowl XLIV was the first Super Bowl matchup in which both teams had a first-round bye since Super Bowl XXXIX.

3. Super Bowl XLIV had 106.5 million viewers on television, making it the third most-watched Super Bowl at the time.

4. The Saints won the coin toss for Super Bowl XLIV, marking the 13th straight Super Bowl the NFC won the toss.

5. Carrie Underwood's performance of the National Anthem marked the third straight year that an alumnus of American Idol has been invited to perform the National Anthem at the Super Bowl. Those other alumni include Jordin Sparks and Jennifer Hudson.

6. The Who's Super Bowl performance was released as downloadable content for the Rock Band video game series, named "The Who Super Bowl S-mashup".

7. Retailers had ordered much more New Orleans Saints merchandise prior to the game than they had ordered Indianapolis Colts merchandise. The NFL estimated that $100 million worth of Super Bowl XLIV merchandise would be sold.

8. Saints place kicker, Garrett Hartley became the first kicker in Super Bowl history to kick three field goals of 40 or more yards in Super Bowl XLIV.

9. The Saints' 25 points scored in the second half is the fourth highest total in Super Bowl history.

10. The New Orleans Saints are the 9th team to win the Super Bowl on their first trip to the Super Bowl.

CHAPTER 14:

HEATED RIVALRIES

QUIZ TIME!

1. Which team does NOT play in the NFC South with the Saints?

    a. Atlanta Falcons

    b. Tennessee Titans

    c. Carolina Panthers

    d. Tampa Bay Buccaneers

2. The New Orleans Saints were a part of the NFC West Division from 1970-2001.

    a. True

    b. False

3. The Saints currently have 1 Super Bowl Championship. How many do the Atlanta Falcons have?

    a. 0

    b. 1

    c. 2

    d. 3

4. The Saints currently have 1 Super Bowl Championship. How many do the Carolina Panthers have?

    a. 0

    b. 1

    c. 2

    d. 3

5. The Saints currently have 1 Super Bowl Championship. How many do the Tampa Bay Buccaneers have?

    a. 0

    b. 1

    c. 2

    d. 3

6. The New Orleans Saints have the most wins among NFC South members.

    a. True

    b. False

7. The Seattle Seahawks currently have the most NFC West Titles of any team in the division.

    a. True

    b. False

8. On January 7, 2018 the New Orleans Saints and the _____ met in the NFL playoffs for the first time in the Wild Card.

    a. Atlanta Falcons

    b. Tampa Bay Buccaneers

    c. Carolina Panthers

    d. San Francisco 49ers

9. In the 2009 NFC Championship game, the New Orleans Saints faced the _____.

   a. Dallas Cowboys
   b. Green Bay Packers
   c. Seattle Seahawks
   d. Minnesota Vikings

10. In the 1991 Wild Card round, the New Orleans Saints faced the _____.

   a. Atlanta Falcons
   b. Tampa Bay Buccaneers
   c. Carolina Panthers
   d. Green Bay Packers

11. The very first game between the Saints and Falcons took place in _____.

   a. 1966
   b. 1967
   c. 1969
   d. 1970

12. The Falcons' longest win streak against the Saints is 10 from 1995-1999.

   a. True
   b. False

13. The very first game between the Saints and Buccaneers took place in _____.

   a. 1975
   b. 1976

c. 1977

d. 1978

14. How many games is the Saints' longest win streak against the Tampa Bay Buccaneers?

    a. 6

    b. 7

    c. 8

    d. 9

15. The Saints won NFC West Championships in 1991 and _____.

    a. 1995

    b. 1999

    c. 2000

    d. 2001

16. From 2002 to 2009, no team in the NFC South earned back-to-back playoff appearances

    a. True

    b. False

17. Which team has the most division championships in the NFC West?

    a. Los Angeles Rams

    b. Arizona Cardinals

    c. Seattle Seahawks

    d. San Francisco 49ers

18. The early 2010's brought much success to both the 49ers and Seahawks due to new head coaches and freshly

drafted quarterbacks. In 2012, the Seahawks drafted QB Russell Wilson. In 2011 the 49ers drafted QB
_____.

a. Alex Smith
b. Jimmy Garoppolo
c. Colin Kaepernick
d. Steve Young

19. A 1977 game between the Bucs and Saints resulted in Tampa Bay's first win in franchise history coming against New Orleans after previously starting out 0–26 overall.

a. True
b. False

20. Every team in the NFC South has made at least one appearance in the Super Bowl.

a. True
b. False

QUIZ ANSWERS

1. B – Tennessee Titans

2. A – True

3. A – 0

4. A – 0

5. B – 1

6. A – True

7. A – True (6)

8. C – Carolina Panthers

9. D – Minnesota Vikings

10. A – Atlanta Falcons

11. B – 1967

12. A – True

13. C – 1977

14. B – 7 (2011-2014)

15. C – 2000

16. True

17. D – San Francisco 49ers (20)

18. C – Colin Kaepernick

19. A – True

20. A – True

DID YOU KNOW?

1. The New Orleans Saints have the most NFC South Championships with 6 total (as of the end of the 2019 season). The Carolina Panthers have 5, the Atlanta Falcons have 4 and the Tampa Bay Buccaneers have 3.

2. "Every year, bus caravans loaded with rowdy (and usually very inebriated) fans make the seven-hour trip between the two cities. Unless you've attended a Falcons-Saints debauchery-filled afternoon, you'll just have to take my word for how much fun it really can be." – Len Pasquarelli

3. The oldest team in the NFC South is the Atlanta Falcons. The Saints came along a year later.

4. New Orleans finished last in the NFC South in 2008 (8–8) and finished first in the NFC South in 2009 (13–3).

5. The NFC South is the only NFL division where no team in the division has swept the division during a regular season.

6. The NFC went under a re-alignment in 2002. The Falcons, Panthers and Saints moved to the NFC South, the Cardinals moved in from the NFC East and the Seahawks returned from the AFC West.

7. In the 2017 NFL season the NFC South had three of its teams qualify for the playoffs (Atlanta, New Orleans, Carolina). Two NFC South teams met in the playoffs; New Orleans hosted the Panthers in the Wild Card playoffs.

8. Each team has won the NFC South at least three times and made a playoff appearance at least three times since the division's formation. The Buccaneers is the only team which has not made the playoffs as a wild-card team.

9. Fans of both the Saints and the Falcons consider the other team their most important and hated opponent.

10. In their last game in the 2014 NFL season, a fight between Saints and Panthers players broke out in the end zone and spilled out into the tunnel entrance after a Cam Newton touchdown.

CHAPTER 15:

THE AWARDS SECTION

QUIZ TIME!

1. Which Saints player won the 2006 Walter Payton NFL Man of the Year Award?

    a. Deuce McAllister
    b. Drew Brees
    c. Reggie Bush
    d. Marques Colston

2. Rickey Jackson was inducted into the New Orleans Saints Hall of Fame in 1997.

    a. True
    b. False

3. Jahri Evans is a ____ Madden Most Valuable Protectors Award winner.

    a. 1x
    b. 2x
    c. 3x
    d. 4x

4. Willie Roaf was a member of the NFL _____ All-Decade Team.

    a. 1990's

    b. 2000's

    c. 2010's

    d. Both A & B

5. Pat Swilling was named the NFL Defensive Player of the Year in _____.

    a. 1987

    b. 1989

    c. 1991

    d. 1992

6. How many ESPN ESPY Awards has Drew Brees won so far in his career (as of the end of the 2019 season)?

    a. 5

    b. 6

    c. 7

    d. 8

7. Sean Payton was named the AP Coach of the Year in 2006.

    a. True

    b. False

8. Which Saints player was named the 2017 Pepsi NFL Rookie of the Year AND the 2017 NFL Offensive Rookie of the Year?

    a. Willie Snead

    b. Alvin Kamara

c. Mark Ingram

d. Wil Lutz

9. Morten Anderson is a ____ winner of the Golden Toe Award.

    a. 1x

    b. 2x

    c. 3x

    d. 4x

10. Mark Ingram Jr. won a Heisman Trophy in _____.

    a. 2008

    b. 2009

    c. 2010

    d. He did not win a Heisman Trophy

11. Jonathan Vilma was named the NFL Defensive Rookie of the Year in _____.

    a. 2004

    b. 2005

    c. 2006

    d. 2007

12. Reggie Bush won the 2005 Heisman Trophy.

    a. True

    b. False

13. Rueben Mayes was named the NFL Offensive Rookie of the Year in _____.

    a. 1983

    b. 1985

c. 1986

d. 1988

14. Ricky Williams won the Heisman Trophy in _____.

    a. 1995

    b. 1996

    c. 1997

    d. 1998

15. What year was Dalton Hilliard inducted into the Louisiana Sports Hall of Fame?

    a. 1993

    b. 1995

    c. 1997

    d. 1999

16. Drew Brees won a Bart Starr Award in 2011.

    a. True

    b. False

17. Which Saints player was named the NFC Defensive Player of the Year in 2000?

    a. Fred McAfee

    b. Sammy Knight

    c. Ricky Williams

    d. La'Roi Glover

18. Morten Andersen was inducted into the Louisiana Sports Hall of Fame in _____.

    a. 2009

    b. 2010

c. 2011

d. 2012

19. Which of the following celebrities has NOT hosted the NFL Honors Awards Show (as of the 2019 season)?

   a. Alec Baldwin
   b. Jimmy Fallon
   c. Seth Meyers
   d. Steve Harvey

20. Pat Swilling was inducted into the New Orleans Saints Hall of Fame in 2000.

   a. True
   b. False

QUIZ ANSWERS

1. B – Drew Brees

2. A – True

3. B – 2x (2009 & 2011)

4. D – Both A & B

5. C – 1991

6. A – 5

7. A – True

8. B – Alvin Kamara

9. B – 2x (1986 & 1995)

10. B – 2009

11. A – 2004

12. B – False, he did win it, but it was later vacated and forfeited by Bush

13. C – 1986

14. D – 1998

15. C – 1997

16. A – True

17. D – La'Roi Glover

18. C – 2011

19. B – Jimmy Fallon

20. A – True

DID YOU KNOW?

1. Drew Brees is a 2x NFL Offensive Player of the Year, Water Payton NFL Man of the Year Award winner, NFL Comeback Player of the Year Award winner, Sports Illustrated Sportsman of the Year, Associated Press Male Athlete of the Year, Bert Bell Award winner, Art Rooney Award winner, Bart Starr Award winner, 2x Best Record Breaking Performance ESPY Award winner, Maxwell Award winner and 2x Big Ten Offensive Player of the Year.

2. Some members of the New Orleans Saints Hall of Fame include Archie Manning, Tom Dempsey, Tony Galbreath, Jim Finks, Doug Atkins, Dave Waymer, Rickey Jackson, Stan Brock, Dalton Hilliard, Sam Mills, Bobby Hebert, Pat Swilling, Jim Mora, Wayne Martin, Rueben Mayes, Willie Roaf, Morten Andersen, Sammy Knight, Deuce McAllister, La'Roi Glover, Aaron Brooks, Will Smith, Jonathan Vilma, Pierre Thomas, Reggie Bush, Marques Colston and Jahri Evans.

3. Michael Lewis was named the NFL Alumni Special Teams Player of the Year in 2002.

4. The NFL hosts an NFL Honors show each year where they give out awards like MVP, Rookie of the Year and Coach of the Year. NFL Honors debuted in Indianapolis in 2012. It is hosted in the city that is hosting the Super Bowl on the network that is carrying that year's Championship game.

5. Archie Manning was named the SEC Player of the Year in 1969.

6. Reggie Bush was named the AP Player of the Year as well as the Sporting News Player of the Year in 2005.

7. Ricky Williams was named the AP Player of the Year as well as the Sporting News Player of the Year in 1998.

8. In addition to being in the New Orleans Saints Hall of Fame, Sam Mills is also in the Carolina Panthers Hall of Honor.

9. Numbers retired by the New Orleans Saints include: Jim Taylor (#31) and Doug Atkins (#81).

10. The New Orleans Saints Ring of Honor contains: Archie Manning, Rickey Jackson, Willie Roaf, Morten Andersen, Tom Benson and Will Smith.

CHAPTER 16:

THE BIG EASY

QUIZ TIME!

1. In 1796, New Orleans became the first city to host a
   _____ in the United States.

   a. Parade
   b. Concert
   c. Block Party
   d. Opera

2. The Superdome is the largest enclosed stadium in the
   world.

   a. True
   b. False

3. Which assassinator was born in New Orleans?

   a. John Wilkes Booth
   b. Mark David Chapman
   c. Lee Harvey Oswald
   d. John Hinckley Jr.

4. Which celebrity was NOT born in New Orleans?

    a. Harry Connick Jr.

    b. Reese Witherspoon

    c. Tyler Perry

    d. Steve Carell

5. What was the name of the serial killer active in New Orleans from May 1918 to October 1919?

    a. The Axeman of New Orleans

    b. The Zodiac

    c. The Knifeman of New Orleans

    d. Jack the Ripper

6. What is the name of New Orleans' signature sweet, pillowy deep fried dough sprinkled with powdered sugar?

    a. Churros

    b. Beignets

    c. Funnel Cake

    d. Conchas

7. Voodoo was introduced to the United States by New Orleans oracle, Marie Laveau.

    a. True

    b. False

8. What is the name of the hurricane that ravaged New Orleans in 2005?

    a. Hurricane Harvey

    b. Hurricane Andrew

    c. Hurricane Sandy

    d. Hurricane Katrina

9. What is the name of New Orleans' MLB team?

    a. New Orleans Panthers
    b. New Orleans Twins
    c. New Orleans Nighthawks
    d. New Orleans does not have an MLB team

10. What is the name of New Orleans' NBA team?

    a. New Orleans Pistons
    b. New Orleans Pelicans
    c. New Orleans Warriors
    d. New Orleans Kings

11. What is the name of the Pelicans' arena?

    a. Little Caesars Arena
    b. Chase Center
    c. Smoothie King Center
    d. Golden 1 Center

12. New Orleans has an NHL team called the New Orleans Jazz.

    a. True
    b. False

13. A newspaper writer gave New Orleans the nickname "The Big Easy" when comparing the easy-going way of life in New Orleans to the hustle and bustle of _____.

    a. Los Angeles
    b. New York City
    c. Chicago
    d. Houston

14. Which famous Disney movie is set in New Orleans?

    a. The Princess and the Frog
    b. Aladdin
    c. Beauty and the Beast
    d. Frozen

15. What is the name of New Orleans' most famous street?

    a. Wall Street
    b. Rodeo Drive
    c. Bourbon Street
    d. Lombard Street

16. The Saint Louis Cathedral is the oldest continually operating cathedral in the United States.

    a. True
    b. False

17. New Orleans' official motto, "Laissez les bons temps rouler!" translates to:

    a. "Live and let go!"
    b. "Let yourself live in the moment!"
    c. "Live crazy live free!"
    d. "Let the good times roll!"

18. What is Louis Armstrong New Orleans International Airport's code?

    a. NOA
    b. LAN
    c. MSY
    d. NOL

19. _____ is the longest continuous bridge over water in the world.

    a. Mackinac Bridge

    b. Lake Ponchartrain Causeway

    c. Golden Gate Bridge

    d. Seven Mile Bridge

20. The Battle of New Orleans was the last major battle in the War of 1812. A treaty had already been signed, but word had not yet reached the soldiers.

    a. True

    b. False

QUIZ ANSWERS

1. D – Opera

2. A - True

3. C – Lee Harvey Oswald

4. D – Steve Carell

5. A – The Axeman of New Orleans

6. B – Beignets

7. True

8. D – Hurricane Katrina

9. D – New Orleans does not have an MLB team

10. B – New Orleans Pelicans

11. C – Smoothie King Center

12. B – False

13. B – New York City

14. A – The Princess and the Frog

15. C – Bourbon Street

16. A – True

17. D – "Let the good times roll!"

18. C – MSY

19. B – Lake Ponchartrain Causeway

20. A – True

DID YOU KNOW?

1. New Orleans was the largest city in the Confederate States of America during the Civil War.

2. Louisiana is the only state in the United States that isn't divided into counties. It is instead broken up into parishes. The greater New Orleans region spans eight parishes.

3. Mardi Gras is held across New Orleans during the two weeks before and through Shrove Tuesday. The actual day of "Mardi Gras" is an official holiday across Louisiana. It's against the law to ride on a New Orleans Mardi Gras float without wearing a mask.

4. In New Orleans, sub sandwiches are known as "po'boys".

5. Most tombs in New Orleans cemeteries are located above ground due to the high-water table of the city. This is the same reason that New Orleans homes do not have basements.

6. There are no traditional West, East, North or South directions in New Orleans. Instead, locals head Uptown, Downtown, Riverside and Lakeside.

7. New Orleans is said to be the most haunted city in the United States.

8. New Orleans dentist, Levi Spear Parmly invented dental floss.

9. There is such a thing in New Orleans as drive-thru daquiri shops.

10. When someone from New Orleans says, "Where y'at?, they aren't asking where you are. They are inquiring about your state of being.

CHAPTER 17:

CITY CHAMP

QUIZ TIME!

1. Where was Rickey Jackson born?

   a. Detroit, Michigan

   b. Pahokee, Florida

   c. Oakland, California

   d. Chicago, Illinois

2. Rickey Jackson played his entire career with the New Orleans Saints.

   a. True

   b. False

3. Where did Rickey Jackson attend college?

   a. University of Florida

   b. University of Pittsburgh

   c. San Diego State University

   d. Florida State University

4. What year was Rickey Jackson inducted into the Pro Football Hall of Fame?

    a. 2007
    b. 2008
    c. 2009
    d. 2010

5. What year was Rickey Jackson inducted into the New Orleans Saints Hall of Fame?

    a. 1996
    b. 1997
    c. 1998
    d. 1999

6. How many Super Bowls did Rickey Jackson win over the course of his NFL career?

    a. 0
    b. 1
    c. 2
    d. 3

7. Rickey Jackson was a Second-Team All-American in 1980.

    a. True
    b. False

8. How many Pro-Bowls was Rickey Jackson named to over the course of his NFL career?

    a. 2
    b. 3
    c. 6
    d. 7

9. Rickey Jackson led the Saints' linebacker corps, nicknamed the "_____".

    a. Crunch Bunch

    b. Monsters of the Midway

    c. Big Gold Wrecking Crew

    d. Dome Patrol

10. Rickey Jackson was drafted by the New Orleans Saints in the _____ round of the 1981 NFL Draft.

    a. 1st

    b. 2nd

    c. 3rd

    d. 4th

11. How many times was Rickey Jackson named a Second-Team All-Pro in his NFL career?

    a. 4

    b. 5

    c. 6

    d. 7

12. Rickey Jackson had 128 total sacks in his NFL career.

    a. True

    b. False

13. How many total interceptions did Rickey Jackson record in his NFL career?

    a. 5

    b. 7

    c. 8

    d. 10

14. What uniform number did Rickey Jackson wear as a member of the New Orleans Saints?

    a. 27
    b. 37
    c. 47
    d. 57

15. What age was Rickey Jackson when he made his NFL debut?

    a. 20
    b. 21
    c. 22
    d. 23

16. Rickey Jackson's uniform number is retired by the New Orleans Saints.

    a. True
    b. False

17. How many total tackles did Rickey Jackson record in his NFL career?

    a. 973
    b. 1,073
    c. 1,173
    d. 1,273

18. When was Rickey Jackson born?

    a. March 20, 1958
    b. March 20, 1968
    c. December 20, 1958
    d. December 20, 1968

19. How many seasons did Rickey Jackson play with the New Orleans Saints?

    a. 10
    b. 12
    c. 13
    d. 15

20. Rickey Jackson's full name is Rickey Anderson Jackson.

    a. True
    b. False

QUIZ ANSWERS

1. B – Pahokee, Florida

2. B – False (Saints and San Francisco 49ers)

3. B – University of Pittsburgh

4. D - 2010

5. B – 1997

6. B – 1 (XXIX with the San Francisco 49ers)

7. A – True

8. C – 6

9. D – Dome Patrol

10. B – 2nd

11. B -5

12. A – True

13. C – 8

14. D – 57

15. D – 23

16. B – False

17. C – 1,173

18. A - March 20, 1958

19. C – 13 (15 total, 2 with SF)

20. A – True

DID YOU KNOW?

1. Rickey Jackson was the first member of the Pro Football Hall of Fame to be inducted primarily for his contributions as a Saint.

2. Jackson's given name is actually spelled "Ricky", but he changed it himself while in high school to "Rickey". He also gave himself his nickname, "City Champ" in high school because of his football performances.

3. In his first year as a finalist, Rickey Jackson was elected to the Pro Football Hall of Fame just one day before the Saints won Super Bowl XLIV in 2010.

4. In his 13 years as a New Orleans Saint, Rickey Jackson only missed two games (due to a car accident).

5. The "Dome Patrol" was named the best linebacking corps in NFL history by NFL Network.

6. Rickey Jackson was named the "NFC Defensive Player of the Week" 5 times in his NFL career. He was named the "NFC Defensive Player of the Month" 2 times in his NFL career.

7. Rickey Jackson played in 227 total games in his NFL career- between the Saints and 49ers.

8. Rickey Jackson was enshrined into the Louisiana Sports Hall of Fame in 1999.

9. At the time of his retirement following the 1995 season, Rickey Jackson held the following NFL records:

10. Second: Most Opponents Fumbles Recovered in Career –
    28

11. Third: Most Sacks in Career – 128.0

12. Tied for third: Most Opponents' Fumbles Recovered in a
    single season – 7 (1990)

13. "Football is the reason for everything I've ever been able to
    have. That's why it's so important to me. It's everything
    for me." – Rickey Jackson

CHAPTER 18:

JAHRI

QUIZ TIME!

1. Where was Jahri Evans born?

    a. San Diego, California

    b. Phoenix, Arizona

    c. Philadelphia, Pennsylvania

    d. Boise, Idaho

2. Jahri Evans played his entire 12 year NFL career with the New Orleans Saints.

    a. True

    b. False

3. When was Jahri Evans born?

    a. April 22, 1989

    b. April 22, 1983

    c. August 22, 1989

    d. August 22, 1983

4. Where did Jahri Evans attend college?

    a. Bloomsburg University of Pennsylvania
    b. University of Florida
    c. University of Alabama
    d. Penn State University

5. How many Pro Bowls was Jahri Evans named to over the course of his NFL career?

    a. 3
    b. 6
    c. 7
    d. 9

6. How many times was Jahri Evans named an First Team All-Pro over the course of his NFL career?

    a. 2
    b. 3
    c. 4
    d. 5

7. Jahri Evans is a 2x Division II All-American.

    a. True
    b. False

8. How many times did Jahri Evans win the Madden Most Valuable Protectors Award?

    a. 0
    b. 1
    c. 2
    d. 4

9. Steve Largent was named a Second Team All-Pro in
   _____.

    a. 2008

    b. 2010

    c. 2012

    d. 2013

10. Jahri Evans was drafted in the _____ round of the 2006
    NFL Draft by the New Orleans Saints.

    a. 1st

    b. 2nd

    c. 3rd

    d. 4th

11. What uniform number did Jahri Evans wear during his
    time with the New Orleans Saints?

    a. 73

    b. 70

    c. 65

    d. 63

12. Jahri Evans did not start playing football until high school.

    a. True

    b. False

13. In 2016, Jahri Evans was a practice squad-only member of
    the _____.

    a. San Francisco 49ers

    b. Seattle Seahawks

    c. Pittsburgh Steelers

    d. Oakland Raiders

14. Jahri Evans graduated in 2007 with a Bachelor's degree in

   _____.

   a. Business
   b. Journalism
   c. English
   d. Exercise Science

15. Jahri Evans was a minority order of which AFL (Arena Football League) team?

   a. Philadelphia Soul
   b. Albany Empire
   c. Atlantic City Blackjacks
   d. All of the Above

16. Jahri Evans is a member of the Omega Psi Phi fraternity.

   a. True
   b. False

17. How many games did Jahri Evans play in over the course of his NFL career?

   a. 163
   b. 173
   c. 183
   d. 193

18. Jahri Evans attended college on an academic scholarship, not an athletic scholarship.

   a. True
   b. False

19. How many Super Bowl Championships did Jahri Evans win in his NFL career?

    a. 0

    b. 1

    c. 2

    d. 3

20. Jahri Evans has a charity called the "Jahri Evans Foundation".

    a. True

    b. False

QUIZ ANSWERS

1. C – Philadelphia, Pennsylvania

2. B – False (Green Bay Packers in 2017)

3. D – August 22, 1983

4. A – Bloomsburg University of Pennsylvania

5. B – 6

6. C – 4

7. A – True (2004, 2005)

8. C – 2 (2009, 2011)

9. D – 2013

10. D – 4th

11. A – 73

12. A – True

13. B – Seattle Seahawks

14. D – Exercise Science

15. D – All of the Above

16. A – True

17. C – 183

18. A – True

19. B – 1 (XLIV)

20. A – True

DID YOU KNOW?

1. Jahri Evans was named as a member of the NFL 2010's All Decade team. He was also named to the Pro Football Weekly All-Rookie Team in 2006.

2. Jahri Evans is a member of the New Orleans Saints 50th Anniversary team, which was announced in 2016.

3. Jahri Evans ranked at #34 on the 2011 NFL Top 100. He ranked at #32 on the 2012 NFL Top 100.

4. In 2009, Jahri Evans established a scholarship at Bloomsburg for out-of-state minority students enrolled in the Master of Science Clinical Athletic Training Program.

5. Jahri Evans was named to the 2010 Pro Bowl NFC roster, becoming only the fourth guard to make the Pro Bowl in the Saints' 43 season history.

6. In May of 2010 the New Orleans Saints signed Jahri Evans to a contract that made him the highest-paid guard in NFL history at the time.

7. Jahri Evans attended Frankford High School in Philadelphia, PA.

8. You can follow Jahri Evans on Twitter @J_7TRE_E

9. Jahri Evans was a finalist for the Division II Gene Upshaw Offensive Player of the Year Award in each of final two seasons at Bloomsburg.

10. In 2013, Jahri Evans married his wife, Takia in the Bahamas.

CONCLUSION

Learn anything new? Now you truly are the ultimate Saints fan! Not only did you learn about the Boys in Black and Gold of the modern era, but you also expanded your knowledge back to the early days of the franchise.

You learned about the Saints' origins and their history, plus about where they came from. You learned about the history of their uniforms and jersey numbers, you identified some famous quotes and read some of the craziest nicknames of all time. You learned more about star quarterback, Drew Brees. You also learned about the legendary Rickey Jackson and Jahri Evans. You were amazed by Saints stats and recalled some of the most infamous Saints trades and drafts / draft picks of all time. You broke down your knowledge by offense, defense and special teams. You looked back on the Saints' championship, playoff feats and the awards that came before, after, and during them. You also learned about the Saints' fiercest rivalries both within their division and out.

Every team in the NFL has a storied history, but the Saints have one of the most memorable of all. They have won a treasured Lombard Trophy with the backing of their devoted fans. Being the ultimate Saints fan takes knowledge and a whole lot of patience, which you tested with this book. Whether you knew every answer or were stumped by several questions, you learned some of the most baffling history that the game of football has to offer.

The deep history of the Saints represents what we all love about the game of football The heart, the determination, the tough times, and the unexpected moments, plus the players that inspire us and encourage us to do our best because even if you get knocked down, there is always another game and another (Sun)day.

With players like Drew Brees, Alvin Kamara and Malcolm Jenkins, the future for the Saints continues to look bright. They have a lot to prove but there is no doubt that this franchise will continue to be one of the most competitive teams in the NFL year after year.

It's a new decade which means there is a clean slate, ready to continue writing the history of the New Orleans Saint. The ultimate Saints fan cannot wait to see what's to come for their beloved Who Dats.

Manufactured by Amazon.ca
Bolton, ON

29907579R00087